kidsource
Combined Words Edition

super songs for church and school
compiled by **Capt. Alan Price, CA**

First published in Great Britain in 2002 by
WORLD WIDE WORSHIP
Buxhall, Stowmarket, Suffolk IP14 3BW
E-mail info@kevinmayhewltd.com

Combined Words
ISBN 1 84003 844 6
ISMN M 57004 981 3
Catalogue No: 1470152

Full Music
ISBN 1 84003 845 4
ISMN M 57004 982 0
Catalogue No: 1470155

9 8 7 6 5 4 3 2 1 0

Cover design by Jonathan Stroulger
Typesetting by Richard Weaver
Proof reader: Linda Ottewell

Printed and bound in Great Britain

Foreword

Christ's message in all its richness must live in your hearts. Teach and instruct each other with all wisdom. Sing psalms, hymns and sacred songs; sing to God with thanksgiving in your hearts.

Colossians 3:16

God continues to inspire Christians to write quality songs for youngsters. Since the compilation of **kidsource**, new songs have been written and new writers are emerging. Alongside this, we are aware of older, traditional songs, hymns and carols that are needed to make as complete a resource as possible at any one time. Today's generation of children needs the songs which express Christian truth in words they can 'own' and in musical styles that are contemporary. Yet we as compilers have a real concern that today's children generally sing few hymns. These are the songs that connect us to our Christian forebears, that are part of our Christian 'folk culture' which reminds us of our heritage.

This is not, however, a book of hymns. It is a complementary resource book, which brings together more of the best songs that work for children of all ages. As with the first volume, the criteria for choice have been that their theological content should be biblically sound, that they should have good, memorable tunes and above all, they should be 'child-friendly'.

There are more of what we term 'cross-over' songs – those written for adults, but which are accessible to children because of their music and lyrical content. It is our belief that many adults will also find these 'children's' songs to be singable without any 'cringe-factor', thus being a collection providing a good resource for all-age worship. Of course there will be songs we have not been able to include, either through ignorance or for copyright reasons.

It is our hope that children's music is performed to the same standard and quality as 'adult' music. Those who play for adults generally rehearse much more than those who play for children. This is in some ways an insult to children, as if they are not worth the effort. So often children's music is regarded with some disdain, as if it is 'lesser' music.

Children are generally uninhibited when it comes to using their bodies in worship. Many songs have actions that reinforce the words, the worship and the celebration of being God's children. It is beyond the scope of this book to attempt to describe such actions, whether they be a simple choreography, or the use of sign language. We would encourage those who use this material to pursue this element of worship, whilst realising that many songs are best sung without physical action.

Music is a major part of life, especially for children. Apart from the almost constant 'background music' surrounding them, the educational value of music is well known as a means of reinforcing teaching. However, music is also a vital means of expressing response to God and his message. Thus **kidsource** has songs suitable for reinforcing biblical teaching on a wide range of topics, and also those songs which will enable children to express their worship and adoration and their desire to follow the Friend and Saviour, Jesus Christ.

CAPT. ALAN PRICE, CA
Compiler

JONATHAN BUGDEN
Adviser

1 Paul Crouch and David Mudie

2 - 4 - 6 - 8, come and join the dance
  and celebrate. Jesus!
1 - 3 - 5 - 7, let's all join in praising
  heaven's high King. Jesus!

1 - 2 - 3 - 4, who's that knocking at the
  door of your heart? Jesus!
5 - 6 - 7 - 8, open up your life before
  it's too late. Jesus!

He'll multiply your blessings and take
  your blues away.
His love heals our divisions and adds
  value to each day.

2 Ian Smale

5 0 0 0 + hungry folk,
5 0 0 0 + hungry folk,
5 0 0 0 + hungry folk
came 4 2 listen 2 Jesus.
The 6 x 2 said O O O,
the 6 x 2 said O O O,
the 6 x 2 said O O O,
where can I get some food from?

Just 1 had 1 2 3 4 5,
just 1 had 1 2 3 4 5,
just 1 had 1 2 3 4 5
loaves and 1 2 fishes.
When Jesus blessed the 5 + 2,
when Jesus blessed the 5 + 2,
when Jesus blessed the 5 + 2
they were increased many x over.

5 0 0 0 + 8 it up,
5 0 0 0 + 8 it up,
5 0 0 0 + 8 it up
with 1 2 3 4 5 6 7 8 9 10 11 12
basketfuls left over.

3 Dave Bilbrough

Abba, Father, let me be
yours and yours alone.
May my will for ever be
more and more your own.
Never let my heart grow cold,
never let me go.
Abba, Father, let me be
yours and yours alone.

4 Noel and Tricia Richards

All heav'n declares
the glory of the risen Lord.
Who can compare
with the beauty of the Lord?
For ever he will be
the Lamb upon the throne.
I gladly bow the knee
and worship him alone.

I will proclaim
the glory of the risen Lord.
Who once was slain
to reconcile us to God.
For ever you will be
the Lamb upon the throne.
I gladly bow the knee
and worship you alone.

5 Graham Kendrick

All I once held dear,
built my life upon,
all this world reveres,
and wars to own,
all I once thought gain
I have counted loss;
spent and worthless now,
compared to this.

Continued overleaf

Knowing you, Jesus, knowing you,
there is no greater thing.
You're my all, you're the best,
you're my joy, my righteousness,
and I love you, Lord.

Now my heart's desire
is to know you more,
to be found in you
and known as yours.
To possess by faith
what I could not earn,
all-surpassing gift
of righteousness.

Oh, to know the pow'r
of your risen life,
and to know you in your sufferings.
To become like you
in your death, my Lord,
so with you to live
and never die.

6 Doug Marks-Smircich

All of my heart, all of my soul,
all of my mind, all of my strength.
All of my heart, all of my soul,
all of my mind, all of my strength.

With ev'rything within me
I want to praise you, Lord.
I want to love you with all that I am,
and bring joy to your heart.

With ev'rything within me
I want to praise you, Lord.
I want to love you with all that I am,
and bring joy to your heart.
Let me bring joy to your heart
all of my life.

7 Paul Crouch and David Mudie

All the creatures of the earth
will declare that you are King.
Ev'ry woman, man and child
confess you Lord of ev'rything.
All creation with one voice,
ev'ry galaxy and star,
in adoration will proclaim
what a holy God you are.

Ev'ry person will bow down,
ev'ry eye will see your face.
When your glory fills the sky,
you will be seen in ev'ry place.
All the people of the world,
ev'rybody near and far,
in adoration will proclaim
what a holy God you are.

8 Cecil Frances Alexander

All things bright and beautiful,
all creatures great and small,
all things wise and wonderful,
the Lord God made them all.

Each little flow'r that opens,
each little bird that sings,
he made their glowing colours,
he made their tiny wings.

The purple-headed mountain,
the river running by,
the sunset and the morning,
that brightens up the sky.

The cold wind in the winter,
the pleasant summer sun,
the ripe fruits in the garden,
he made them ev'ry one.

He gave us eyes to see them,
and lips that we may tell
how great is God Almighty,
who has made all things well.

9 John Newton

Amazing grace! How sweet the sound
that saved a wretch like me.
I once was lost, but now I'm found;
was blind, but now I see.

'Twas grace that taught my heart to fear,
and grace my fears relieved.
How precious did that grace appear
the hour I first believed.

Through many dangers, toils and snares
I have already come.
'Tis grace that brought me safe thus far,
and grace will lead me home.

The Lord has promised good to me,
his word my hope secures;
he will my shield and portion be
as long as life endures.

When we've been there a thousand
  years,
bright shining as the sun,
we've no less days to sing God's praise
than when we first begun.

10 Karen Porter

A million stars are in the sky,
how great is God, how small am I.
This vast expanse, at his command,
and yet my future is in his hands.

He is so great,
he is so mighty,
and yet he cares
for someone like me.
He is so great,
he is so mighty,
eternal God and Father is he!

Great King of kings, he reigns on high,
ruler of earth, and sea and sky.
A tiny bird falls from a tree,
God sees it all, and he knows me.

He sent his own Son to save me,
he died so I could be free.
He is so great . . .

Eternal God and Father is he!

11 J. W. Wood

And God said the sun should shine,
the rain should fall, the flowers should
  grow;
and God said the birds should sing,
and it was so, was so.

And God said the grass should grow,
the trees bear fruits, the winds should
  blow;
and God said the streams should flow,
and it was so, was so.

12 Jim Bailey

As for me and my house,
as for me and my family,
as for me and my children,
we will serve the Lord.
As for me and my house,
as for me and my family,
as for me and my children,
we will serve the Lord.

Continued overleaf

In this family,
we're gonna do things properly,
read God's word ev'ry day
and then we'll try to pray;
although we get it wrong,
we will still carry on,
make Jesus number one
in this place.
In this place we're gonna say grace.

As for me and my house,
as for me and my family,
as for me and my children,
we will serve the Lord.
As for me and my house,
as for me and my family,
as for me and my children,
we will serve the Lord.

13   Paul Crouch and David Mudie

As we share bread in the family of God,
we think of Jesus, God's Son.
Died in our place as the payment for sin.
We adore you and worship you now.

Jesus, our Saviour,
ruler in power,
we come now
and give you our praise.
(Repeat)

As we share wine in the family of God,
we think of Jesus, God's Son.
Rose from the dead in victory and
    power.
We adore you and worship you now.

14   William Chatterton Dix alt. Roger Jones

As with gladness men of old
did the guiding star behold,
as with joy they hailed its light,
leading onward beaming bright.

So, most gracious God, may we
evermore be led to thee.

As with joyful steps they sped
to that lowly manger bed,
there to bend the knee before
him whom heav'n and earth adore.

As they offered gifts most rare,
at that manger rude and bare,
so may we with holy joy
pure and free from sin's alloy.

Holy Jesus, ev'ry day
keep us in the narrow way,
and when earthly things are past
save our ransomed souls at last.

15   William James Kirkpatrick

Away in a manger,
no crib for a bed,
the little Lord Jesus
laid down his sweet head.
The stars in the bright sky
looked down where he lay,
the little Lord Jesus,
asleep on the hay.

The cattle are lowing,
the baby awakes,
but little Lord Jesus
no crying he makes.
I love thee, Lord Jesus!
Look down from the sky,
and stay by my side
until morning is nigh.

Be near me, Lord Jesus;
I ask thee to stay
close by me for ever,
and love me, I pray.
Bless all the dear children
in thy tender care,
and fit us for heaven,
to live with thee there.

16   Paul Field

A wiggly, waggly worm, a slipp'ry, slimy
   slug,
a creepy, crawly, buzzy thing, a tickly,
   wickly bug;
of all the things to be, I'm happy that
   I'm me.
Thank you, Lord, I'm happy that I'm me.
I'm happy that I'm me, happy that I'm
   me.
There's no one else in all the world that
   I would rather be.
A wiggly, waggly worm, a slippery, slimy
   slug,
a creepy, crawly, buzzy thing, a tickly,
   wickly bug.

A prickly porcupine, a clumsy kangaroo,
a croaky frog, a hairy hog, a monkey in a
   zoo;
of all the things to be, I'm happy that
   I'm me.
Thank you, Lord, I'm happy that I'm me.
I'm happy that I'm me, happy that I'm
   me.
There's no one else in all the world that
   I would rather be.
A prickly porcupine, a clumsy kangaroo,
a croaky frog, a hairy hog, a monkey in a
   zoo.

17   Morris Chapman

Be bold, be strong,
for the Lord, your God, is with you.
Be bold, be strong,
for the Lord, your God, is with you.
I am not afraid, I am not dismayed,
because I'm walking in faith and victory,
come on and walk in faith and victory,
for the Lord, your God, is with you.

18   Capt. Alan Price, CA

Because of who he is,
because of who he is,
because of all he's done,
because of all he's done,
because of all his love for us,
we worship the Three in One.

We have come to God the Father,
we have come to God the Father,
in the name of God the Son,
in the name of God the Son,
by the power of the Spirit,
we worship the Three in One.

Because of who you are,
because of who you are,
because of all you've done,
because of all you've done,
because of all your love for us,
we worship the Three in One.

19 David J. Evans

Be still, for the presence of the Lord,
the Holy One is here.
Come, bow before him now,
with reverence and fear.
In him no sin is found,
we stand on holy ground.
Be still, for the presence of the Lord,
the Holy One is here.

Be still, for the glory of the Lord
is shining all around;
he burns with holy fire,
with splendour he is crowned.
How awesome is the sight,
our radiant King of light!
Be still, for the glory of the Lord
is shining all around.

Be still, for the power of the Lord
is moving in this place;
he comes to cleanse and heal,
to minister his grace.
No work too hard for him,
in faith receive from him.
Be still, for the power of the Lord
is moving in this place.

©1986 Kingsway's Thankyou Music

20 Capt. Alan Price, CA

Be the centre of my life, Lord Jesus,
be the centre of my life I pray;
be my Saviour to forgive me,
be my friend to be with me,
be the centre of my life today!

Let the power of your presence, Lord Jesus,
from the centre of my life shine through;
oh, let ev'rybody know it,
I really want to show it,
that the centre of my life is you!

© 1990 Daybreak Music Ltd

21 Judy Bailey

Calling on the Spirit (calling on the Spirit),
Holy Spirit (Holy Spirit),
come down to us (come down to us)
in fire and rain (in fire and rain).
Fire brings us holiness (fire brings us
holiness),
purity and passion (purity and passion),
rain revives us (rain revives us),
gives us hope again.

We've been waiting, now's the time,
hear our hearts, hear our cry.
Let the Spirit move on ev'ryone,
let the fire fall, let the rain come down.
Let the fire fall, and let the rain come;
let the fire fall, and let the rain come;
let the fire fall, and let the rain come
down.

© Ice Music Ltd, Barbados

22 Capt. Alan Price, CA

Can we love one another
just like Jesus has loved us,
can we do what he commands?
Can we love other people
just as we love ourselves,
or is it just too much to demand?

Yes, we can and we will!
yes, we can and we will!
even if sometimes it's hard.
Yes, we can and we will!
yes, we can and we will!
even if sometimes it's hard.

Yes, we can and we will!
yes, we can and we will!
even if sometimes we fail and let him
down.
Yes, we can and we will!
yes, we can and we will!
even if sometimes we fail.

Yes, we can and we will!
yes, we can and we will!
even if sometimes we fail and let him
    down.
Yes, we can and we will!
yes, we can and we will!
even if sometimes we fail
(God will help us).
We will love one another
just like Jesus has loved us,
and we will do what he commands!

23 Paul Field

Can you count the stars shining in the
    sky?
Can you hold the moonlight in your hand?
Can you stop the waves rolling on the
    shore?
Or find the place where rainbows meet
    the land?

*I've got a friend who knows
how all these things are done.
Jesus, Lord of all, God's only Son.*

Up in outer space, planets spinning
    round,
millions more than we can ever see.
It's hard to understand how God,
    who made it all,
still cares about someone like you
    and me.

24 Graham Kendrick

Can you see what we have made
for this very special day?
An orange for our planet home
circling around the sun.

Count the seasons as we sing,
summer, autumn, winter, spring.
Sing to God who sends the rain,
making all things new again.

*Candle light, burning bright,
chase the darkness of the night.
Christ the light, light our way,
live inside our hearts today.*

See the food with colours bright,
tastebuds tingle at the sight.
Let's be thankful as we share,
God's good gifts are ev'rywhere.

Why then is the world we made,
wrapped around with ribbon red?
Red is for the ransom paid,
when our Lord was crucified.

There's a world I'm dreaming of,
where there's peace and joy and love.
Light of Jesus ev'rywhere,
this is my Christingle prayer.

25 Gary Oliver

Celebrate Jesus, celebrate!
Celebrate Jesus, celebrate!
Celebrate Jesus, celebrate!
Celebrate Jesus, celebrate!
He is risen, he is risen,
and he lives for evermore.
He risen, he is risen,
come on and celebrate
the resurrection of our Lord.

26 Capt. Alan Price, CA

*Christmas, it's Christmas,
it's Christmas once again.
The birthday of Jesus,
born in Bethlehem.*

Continued overleaf

The Lord, who was that tiny baby,
existed long before the birth.
He laid aside his heav'nly glory
to be Jesus, Saviour of the earth!

Christmas, it's Christmas,
it's Christmas once again.
The birthday of Jesus,
born in Bethlehem.

The Lord, who was that tiny baby,
grew up and lived to show the Father's
love.
He laid aside his life to bring us back to
God,
raised to life, he's back in heaven
above.

Christmas, it's Christmas,
it's Christmas once again.
We thank you, Lord Jesus,
that you came. Amen.

27 Robyn Barnett

Church is not a building,
it's the people there inside;
people who love Jesus
and wear his badge with pride.
Though he's gone to heaven,
he's left us in his place,
to be his body here on earth,
his hands, his feet, his face . . .

28 Paul Crouch and David Mudie

C - L - A - P, clap my hands.
J - U - M - P, jump!
Yes, yes, S - T - A - M - P my feet,
for J - E - S - U - S!
Jesus is the B - E - S - T friend that you
could know.
He will always be with you, wherever
you G - O.

29 Tom Daniel, Bob Buzbee, Ernie Rettino, Debbie Kerner

Clap your hands, stomp your feet,
spread the love of Jesus to ev'ryone
you meet.
Oh! Clap your hands, stomp your feet,
spread a little love around.

The love of Jesus is a sweet, sweet song,
that you can give to others as you walk
along.
With a smile on your face, and his love
in your heart,
you spread the love of Jesus, now
everybody start to

The love of Jesus is a miracle
God has given ev'ry boy and girl.
His Son came to earth because he loves
us so,
and now it's up to us to let his miracle
show. Oh!

30 Yvonne Scott

Come along, ev'ryone, let's worship God
together.
Come along, ev'ryone, let's worship God
together.
Ev'ry girl, ev'ry boy, let's worship God
together.
Praise, praise, praise, praise, praise
together.

31 Mark and Helen Johnson

*Come and join in the song,
Jesus Christ is Lord over all,
and he lives to reign for evermore.
The heavens applaud: 'He's alive!
He's alive!'*

*Lift your hearts and your voices,
fill the earth with rejoicing for*

He's ascended to the skies,
in heaven now he reigns.
Lord of glory, Lord of life,
he will return again.

Ev'ry knee shall bow to him,
and ev'ryone confess:
Jesus Christ is Lord and King,
he's conquered sin and death!

Ev'ry nation, ev'ry tribe
will glorify his name.
All creation shall bow down
and honour him with praise!

*Come and join in the song,
Jesus Christ is Lord over all,
and he lives to reign for evermore.
The heavens applaud: 'He's alive!
He's alive! He's alive! He's alive!'*

32 Mike Burn

Come and sing, come and sing,
come and sing to Jesus now.
Come and sing, come and sing,
come and sing to Jesus now.
Give him thanks for who he is,
give him thanks for what he's done,
come and sing.

*Jesus won it all for us
when he shed his blood on the cross.
Sin and death were swallowed up,
they don't have a hold on us now,
that's the reason to sing.*

Come and dance, come and dance,
come and dance for Jesus now.
Come and dance, come and dance,
come and dance for Jesus now.
Dance for joy before the throne,
let your inhibitions go,
come and dance.

33 Chris Jackson

Come, Jesus, come,
touch my heart with a deep compassion.
Lord, I want to see,
I want to feel what you feel.
Fill me with love,
fill me with pow'r,
send your Holy Spirit.
Come, Lord Jesus, come.

34 Patricia Morgan and Dave Bankhead

Come on and celebrate
his gift of love, we will celebrate
the Son of God who loved us
and gave us life.
We'll shout your praise, O King,
you give us joy nothing else can bring,
we'll give to you our offering
in celebration praise.

Come on and celebrate, celebrate,
celebrate and sing,
celebrate and sing to the King.
Come on and celebrate, celebrate,
celebrate and sing,
celebrate and sing to the King.

35 Ian White

Crackers and turkeys and pudding and
    cream,
toys in the windows that I've never seen.
This is the Christmas that ev'ryone sees,
but Christmas means more to me.

It's somebody's birthday I won't forget,
as I open the things that I get.
I'll remember the inn and the stable so
    bare,
and Jesus who once lay there.

Ev'ryone's out shopping late ev'ry night,
for candles and presents and Christmas
    tree lights.
This is the Christmas that ev'ryone sees,
but Christmas means more to me.

Christmas morning, the start of the day,
there's presents to open and new games
    to play.
This is the Christmas that ev'ryone sees,
but Christmas means more to me.

36 Ian Smale

Dear Lord, my Father who's in heav'n,
honoured be your holy name.
May your kingdom come,
may your will be done,
here on earth as it is in heav'n.
Dear Lord, please give us food today,
and forgive us as we forgive others.
May your testing be not too hard to bear,
and deliver us from the evil one.
Amen, amen, amen, amen.
Amen, amen, amen, amen.

37 Doug Horley

Do not worry, oh, do not worry, oh,
do not worry, oh, 'bout anything.
(Repeat)

Do not worry about anything
but pray and ask God for ev'rything you
    need,
and when you pray, oh,
always give thanks
and the peace of God will keep your
    mind in Jesus.

Does worry ever stop bad things
    happening?
No, and it won't help make them go away.
Will worry ever, ever, ever help you get
    better
when you're really, really, really, really
    sick? No way!
Worry won't help when the going gets
    tough,
worry won't help when life is really rough,
but instead of prayin' last and panicking
    fast,
don't worry in a hurry, turn to Jesus,
turn to Jesus, turn to Jesus. Oh, turn to
    Jesus.

38 Sammy Horner

Don't be afraid or put off,
just trust with all your might,
stand up, speak out
and live for the things of God.
So if you're scared, or let down,
just learn from what's gone on,
stand up, speak out
and live for the things of God.

Doesn't matter if you're young or old,
or if you're rich or poor;
there's no easy way to live for God,
of that you can be sure.

Doesn't matter if you're big or small,
strong or insecure;
there's no easy way to live for God,
of that you can be sure.

© 1995 Daybreak Music Ltd

39 Nick Harding

Don't be an actor, don't be a fraud,
'cos you might fool others
but you won't fool the Lord.
Don't be a show-off, don't do an act,
'cos it's your heart, heart, heart that
matters,
and that's a fact!

You can dress up smart, you can dress
up rough,
you can try to act big, you can try to act
tough,
but after a while you'll have had enough,
and what good would that do?

You can act happy when you're feeling
down,
you can put on a smile when your face
wants to frown,
you know it's no use trying to be a
clown,
just be the real 'you'.

© 1995 Daybreak Music Ltd

40 Karen Lafferty

Don't build your house on the sandy
land,
don't build it too near the shore.
Well, it might look kind of nice,
but you'll have to build it twice,
oh, you'll have to build your house once
more.
You'd better * build your house upon a
rock,
make a good foundation on a solid spot.
Oh, the storms may come and go,
but the peace of God you will know.

*If sung as a round the second group of
voices enters here.*

© 1981 Maranatha! Music/Copy Care

41 Ralph Chambers

Don't know much about the ozone layer,
rain forests seem miles away,
but each of us can be a player,
fight to save the world God has made.
This is God's world, this is God's world,
and you're a member of the human race.
This is God's world, this is God's world,
let's try to make it a better place.

© 1991 Daybreak Music Ltd

42 Merrilyn Billing

Don't repay evil for evil,
don't snap back at those
who say unkind things about you.
(Repeat)

Instead, pray, pray for God's help for them,
for we are to be kind to others.
Pray, pray for God's help for them,
and God will bless us for it.

Pray, pray for God's help for them,
for we are to be kind to others.
Pray, pray for God's help for them,
and God will bless us for it.

43 Judy MacKenzie Dunn

Don't you worry about tomorrow,
where you'll be or what you'll say.
He'll take care of your tomorrow
if you just follow him today.

Where shall I go, what should I say,
how do I know which is the way?
Facing the future, feeling afraid,
time to remember what Jesus said.

When days are dark and nights are long,
when times are hard and things go wrong,
he'll never leave you, he won't let you
    down,
he's there to lead you to solid ground.

44 Paul Field

Down in the jungle on a Saturday night,
all the animals get together,
to talk about the things that man has
    done
to change the world for ever.
The wonders of creation die
from greed and from pollution,
if man's supposed to be so smart
then where is the solution?
All things bright and beautiful,
all creatures great and small,
but the trouble with man just seems to be
he doesn't care at all.

When God made ev'ry living thing
he made the world for sharing.
He wants us all to get along
by loving and by caring.
A perfect earth for ev'ryone
that we should be enjoying,
so how is it that we have come
to spoiling and destroying?
All things wise and wonderful,
the Lord God made them all.
The trouble with man just seems to be
that he won't share at all.

The trouble with me and the trouble
    with you,
we want so much that we don't need,
sooner or later we've got to see
and live together, like it's meant to be.

45 Mark and Helen Johnson

Easter jubilation fills the streets and
    towns,
celebrations have begun.
Hear the music and the dancing now,
join the laughter and the fun!

Oh, raise a joyful shout!
Clap your hands and dance,
let your feelings out.
Oh, hear what it's about:
Christ, the Lord, has come
*to set us free. *Hoy!*

Put aside your sorrows, wipe your tears
     away,
for a better time will come.
There's a promise of a better day,
join the laughter and the fun!

La, la, la, la, la, etc.

Easter jubilation fills the streets and towns,
celebrations have begun.
Hear the music and the dancing now,
join the laughter and the fun!

* Last time only

46   Doug Horley

Ev'rybody has a wobble from time to
*   time,*
ev'rybody has some shake, rattle and
*   roll in their lives.*
Ev'rybody has a wobble from time to
*   time,*
ev'rybody has some shake, rattle and
*   roll in their lives.*

It's not wrong to have some questions,
it's not wrong to have some doubts,
but sometimes we need help
from our friends to work things out.
To the promises he's made us,
we must learn to hold on tight,
'cos no way will he leave us,
even in the darkest night.

47   Ian Smale

Ev'ry day with Jesus,
ev'ry day with Jesus,
ev'ry day with Jesus,
I want to spend my ev'ry day with him.

I realise the Bible is a book I need to
     read,
it shows me how my Christian life can
     start.
Then as I get older, just like a healthy
     food,
it strengthens me when I hide it in my
     heart.

I realise the Bible is a book I need to
     read,
and ev'ry page I read I know is true.
For God has breathed upon his book to
     help me ev'ry day,
and show me what's his plan for me
     to do.

I realise the Bible is a book I need to
     read,
the more I read the more I'm going to
     know,
about things of importance and how my
     life should be,
it's what a Christian needs to make
     things grow.

48   Ian White

Ev'rywhere he walks with me,
and through prayer he talks with me.
He has cared enough for me,
to die, to set me free.

Since then you have been raised with
     Christ,
set your hearts on things above.
Where Christ is seated at God's right
     hand,
set your minds on things above.

Continued overleaf

Ev'rywhere he walks with me,
and through prayer he talks with me.
He has cared enough for me,
to die, to set me free.

Put to death whatever is sin,
rid yourself of all these things.
You have been renewed in the Lord,
and he is all, and is in all.

Let his peace now rule in your hearts.
Let his Word be rich in you.
Sing psalms and hymns with thanks to
   God,
praise him in all that you do.

49   Graham Kendrick

Far and near hear the call,
worship him, Lord of all;
families of nations, come,
celebrate what God has done.

Deep and wide is the love
heaven sent from above;
God's own Son, for sinners died,
rose again – he is alive.

   Say it loud, say it strong,
   tell the world what God has done;
   say it loud, praise his name,
   let the earth rejoice –
   for the Lord reigns.

At his name, let praise begin;
oceans roar, nature sing,
for he comes to judge the earth
in righteousness and in his truth.

50   Capt. Alan Price, CA

Father God, I come to you
and wonder at your love,
that you knew me,
and you cared for me
before the world was made;
and I stand and think
and love to feel
your love so deep inside,
and to know for sure
your love for me
will never, ever fade.

51   Yvonne Scott

Father God, I know you love me so,
Father God, I know you care for me.
Father God, I know you love me so,
Father God, I'm small but you care
   for me.

Father God, I'm small but I love you so,
Father God, I'm small but I'll follow you.
Father God, I'm small but I love you so,
Father God, I'm small but I'll follow you.

52   Ian Smale

Father God, I wonder
how I managed to exist
without the knowledge of your
   parenthood
and your loving care.
But now I am your child,
I am adopted in your family
and I can never be alone
'cause, Father God, you're there beside
   me.

I will sing your praises,
I will sing your praises,
I will sing your praises,
for evermore.
I will sing your praises,
I will sing your praises,
I will sing your praises,
for evermore.

53 Paul Crouch and David Mudie

Father God, you love me and you know
  me inside out.
You know the words that I will say
  before I speak them out.
You are all around me, you hold me in
  your hand.
Your love for me is more than I can ever
  understand.

Father God, from your love there is
  nowhere I can hide.
If I go down into the depths or cross the
  ocean wide,
there your love would find me, you'd
  take me in your hand.
Your love for me is more than I can ever
  understand.

54 Danny Daniels

Father, I can call you Father,
for I am your child
today, tomorrow and always,
you are my Father.

Father, how I love you,
Father, I will sing your praise,
today, tomorrow and always,
for you're my Father.

*Father, Father, Father, to me.
Father, holy Father, Father to me.*

Father, I will serve you,
Father, I will seek your face
today, tomorrow and always,
you are my Father.

55 Judy Bailey and Dave Bankhead

Father, I do adore you,
worship before you,
I love you, Lord.
(Repeat)

> *You have opened up my eyes
> to see such beauty in your face,
> a love that cared enough to set
>   me free;
> and my heart is filled with wonder
> at the glory of your grace,
> I'm so thankful, Lord,
> that now you live in me.*

Jesus, I do adore you . . .

Spirit, I do adore you . . .

56 Yvonne Scott

Father, I thank you with my voice,
la-la-la, la-la-la.
Father, I thank you with my voice,
with my voice.

Father, I thank you with my hands,
with my hands, with my hands.
Father, I thank you with my hands,
with my hands.
*(Each time the words 'with my hands'
  are sung, then clap hands)*

Continued overleaf

Father, I thank you with my feet,
with my feet, with my feet.
Father, I thank you with my feet,
with my feet.
*(Each time the words 'with my feet' are
sung, then jump or dance)*

Father, I thank you with my voice,
with my hands, with my feet.
Father, I thank you with my voice,
hands and feet.
*('With my voice' – no action, 'with my
hands' – clap, 'with my feet' –
jump/dance)*

57 Terrye Coelho

Father, we adore you,
lay our lives before you,
how we love you.

Jesus, we adore you . . .

Spirit, we adore you . . .

58 Paul Crouch and David Mudie

Father, your word is like a light in the
darkness.
Father, your word is like a sharp, sharp
sword.
Father, your word is like a stream in the
desert.
There's nothing that compares with the
wisdom of your word.

59 Paul Field

Find the silence through the noise,
listen to the Saviour's voice,
he is calling you, calling you to come.
Don't turn away, don't close your eyes,
you need his love to fill your life.
He is calling you, calling you to come.
He is reaching out to be by your side,
he will be your friend for life.

> *Give him your heart, give him your
> heart.*
> *You will find out that life really starts
> when you give him your heart.*

You may be good, you may be bad,
you may be happy, you may be sad,
still he is calling you,
calling you to come.
Find the silence through the noise,
listen to the Saviour's voice,
he is calling you,
calling you to come.
He is reaching out to be by your side,
he will be your friend for life.

60 Nick Harding

> *For ever I will live my life by faith;
> I'm always gonna live my life by faith.
> For ever I will live my life by faith;
> I'm always gonna live my life by faith.*

By faith I can obey,
by faith I praise and pray,
by faith I am made new,
by faith I know it's true.

By faith I take God's hand,
by faith I understand,
by faith I am made pure,
by faith I can be sure.

61 Dave Richards

For I'm building a people of power
and I'm making a people of praise,
that will move through this land by my
   Spirit,
and will glorify my precious name.
Build your church, Lord,
make us strong, Lord,
join our hearts, Lord,
through your Son.
Make us one, Lord, in your body,
in the kingdom of your Son.

62 Graham Kendrick

From heav'n you came, helpless babe,
entered our world, your glory veiled;
not to be served but to serve,
and give your life that we might live.

   This is our God, the Servant King,
   he calls us now to follow him,
   to bring our lives as a daily offering
   of worship to the Servant King.

There in the garden of tears,
my heavy load he chose to bear;
his heart with sorrow was torn.
'Yet not my will but yours,' he said.

Come, see his hands and his feet,
the scars that speak of sacrifice,
hands that flung stars into space,
to cruel nails surrendered.

So let us learn how to serve,
and in our lives enthrone him;
each other's needs to prefer,
for it is Christ we're serving.

63 Richard Hubbard

F - U - N - E - N - R - G?
Come and praise the Lord with me.
O - I - C - Y - M - 2 - B
filled with joy and victor - E.
F - U - N - E - N - R - G?
S - V - F - Z - N - R - G.
J - E - S - U - S for me,
S - S - Y - I - M so 3.

F - U - F - N - 10 - E bounce,
& U - F - N - 10 - E go,
come 2 J - E - S - U - S,
E - L give U zap 2 glow.
O - I - 8 - 2 - C - U sad,
& I - 8 - 2 - C - U low,
U - C - U - R - O - K 2 God,
& E wants 2 - C - U grow!

The interpretation

Have you any energy?
Come and praise the Lord with me.
Oh, I see why I'm to be
filled with joy and victory.
Have you any energy?
'Yes, we have the energy.'
J - E - S - U - S for me,
this is why I am so free.

If you haven't any bounce,
and you haven't any go,
come to J - E - S - U - S,
he will give you zap to glow.
Oh, I hate to see you sad,
and I hate to see you low,
you see you are OK to God,
and he wants to see you grow!

64 Capt. Alan Price, CA

Get on board! the Kingdom train is
    moving.
Get on board! hear the whistle blow.
Get on board! if you want to follow
    Jesus,
sh, sh, woo woo, it's time to go.
Woo woo! we'll keep on moving.
Woo woo! to the journey's end.
Woo woo! by the power of the Spirit,
we're travelling with Jesus on the
    Kingdom train.

Last time
We're travelling with Jesus,
we're travelling with Jesus,
we're travelling with Jesus on the
    Kingdom train.

© 1996 Daybreak Music Ltd

I'll sing the songs of salvation,
boldly I'll speak out your word.
I'll let them know by my life,
I will show you are Lord.
I'll tell them all about Jesus,
I'll tell them all about you,
I'm not ashamed of the gospel
or what it can do.

We're moving forward together,
as one voice boldly proclaim,
the old and the young will be strong,
and we'll lift up your name
on to the streets to the people,
ev'ry man, woman and child,
and as we go you are with us,
you've given your pow'r.

You've enabled your servants . . .

© 1997 Kingsway's Thankyou Music

65 Jim Bailey

Give me a heart of compassion,
give me a hope for the lost.
Give me a passion for those
who are broken and down.
Lord, I am ready and willing
to serve the weak and the young.
Help me to put into action
the words of this song.

And enable your servants,
enable your servants to preach good
    news,
to preach good news.
(Repeat)

66 Traditional

Give me oil in my lamp, keep me
    burning.
Give me oil in my lamp, I pray.
Give me oil in my lamp, keep me
    burning,
keep me burning till the break of day.

Sing hosanna, sing hosanna,
sing hosanna to the King of kings!
Sing hosanna, sing hosanna,
sing hosanna to the King!

Give me joy in my heart, keep me
    singing.
Give me joy in my heart, I pray.
Give me joy in my heart, keep me
    singing,
keep me singing till the break of day.

Give me love in my heart, keep me
    serving.
Give me love in my heart, I pray.
Give me love in my heart, keep me
    serving,
keep me serving till the break of day.

Give me peace in my heart, keep me
    resting.
Give me peace in my heart, I pray.
Give me peace in my heart, keep me
    resting,
keep me resting till the break of day.

67 Yvonne Scott

Gives! Gives! Gives!
That's what God does.
Gives! Gives! Gives!
That's what God does each day.
Great! Great! Great!
God is very great.

Thanks! Thanks! Thanks!
That's what we say.
Thanks! Thanks! Thanks!
That's what we say each day.
Great! Great! Great!
God is very great.

68 Henry Smith

Give thanks with a grateful heart.
Give thanks to the Holy One.
Give thanks because he's given
Jesus Christ, his Son.
Give thanks with a grateful heart.
Give thanks to the Holy One.
Give thanks because he's given
Jesus Christ, his Son.

And now let the weak say, 'I am strong',
let the poor say, 'I am rich',
because of what the Lord has done for
    us.
And now let the weak say, 'I am strong',
let the poor say, 'I am rich',
because of what the Lord has done for
    us.

Give thanks.

69 Danny Daniels

Glory, glory in the highest;
glory to the Almighty;
glory to the Lamb of God,
and glory to the living Word;
glory to the Lamb!
(Repeat)
I give glory (glory),
glory (glory),
glory, glory to the Lamb!
I give glory (glory),
glory (glory),
glory, glory to the Lamb!
I give glory to the Lamb!

70 Capt. Alan Price, CA

God always has time for us,
he will always listen.
God always has time for us,
time for evr'yone.
He cares for you
and he cares for me,
he isn't too busy, is he?
No! He cares for you
and he cares for me,
he isn't too busy, is he? No!

Continued overleaf

God always has time for us,
he will always listen.
God always has time for us,
time for ev'ryone.
He cares for you
and he cares for me,
he isn't too busy, is he?
No! He cares for you
and he cares for me,
he isn't too busy for us!

71   Paul Crouch and David Mudie

God has a perfect plan for me,
God has a perfect plan for me.
Following Jesus is where I want to be,
God has a perfect plan for me.
He knows the end from the beginning,
he sees the path I need to take.
I have a part to play in God's
    amazing plan,
so I will try to follow him each day.

You have a perfect plan for me,
you have a perfect plan for me.
Following you, Lord, is where I want
    to be,
you have a perfect plan for me.
You know the end from the beginning,
you see the path I need to take.
I have a part to play in your
    amazing plan,
so help me, Lord, to follow you
    each day.

God has a perfect plan for you,
God has a perfect plan for you.
To follow Jesus – that's what we want
    to do,
God has a perfect plan for you.
God has a perfect plan for me,
God has a perfect plan for me.

Following Jesus is where I want to be,
God has a perfect plan for, his perfect
    plan is best for,
God has a perfect plan for me.

72   Chris Jackson

God is faithful,
he is the one.
God is faithful,
he's the one
who has called us
to share life with his Son,
Jesus Christ our Lord.

73   Capt. Alan Price, CA

God is good, God is great,
he's the one who did create
ev'rything that there is by his power.
God is good, God is great,
he's the one who did create
ev'rything that there is by his power.

Thank you, Lord, for the things I can see,
thank you, thank you, Lord.
Thank you, Lord, for the sounds I can hear,
thank you, thank you, Lord.

Thank you, Lord, for my family,
thank you, thank you, Lord.
Thank you, Lord, for all my friends,
thank you, thank you, Lord.

Thank you, Lord, for the birds in the sky,
thank you, thank you, Lord.
Thank you, Lord, for the ants on the
    ground,
thank you, thank you, Lord.

Thank you, Lord, for your love to me,
thank you, thank you, Lord.
Thank you, Lord, that you're always near,
thank you, thank you, Lord.

74 Graham Kendrick

God is good, we sing and shout it,
God is good, we celebrate.
God is good, no more we doubt it,
God is good, we know it's true.

And when I think of his love for me,
my heart fills with praise
and I feel like dancing.
For in his heart there is room for me
and I run with arms opened wide.

75 Ian Smale

God is here, God is here,
Almighty God is here.
Bow down before him
in reverence and fear.
God is here, God is here,
Almighty God is here,
Almighty God is here.

It's hard to imagine how it could ever be
that the maker of the universe is now
    here with me.
I'll no longer live in loneliness, nor fear
    the enemy.
Almighty God is here.

As I see my generation in sadness and
    in pain,
I hear the fools say, 'There's no God',
    time and time again.
But fools can never change the fact that
    our God is here to reign.
Almighty God is here.

So let's call together all the saints, their
    voices to proclaim
that the Father, Son and Spirit will
    forever be the same,
and the day will come when every knee
    shall bow at Jesus' name.
Almighty God is here.

76 Ian Smale

God is here, God is present,
God is moving by his Spirit.
Can you hear what he is saying,
are you willing to respond?
God is here, God is present,
God is moving by his Spirit.
Lord, I open up my life to you,
please do just what you will.
Lord, I won't stop loving you,
you mean more to me than anyone else.
Lord, I won't stop loving you,
you mean more to me than anyone else.

77 Alex Simons and Freda Kimmey

God is our Father,
for he has made us his own,
made Jesus our brother,
and hand in hand we'll grow together as
    one.
Sing praise to the Lord with the
    tambourine,
sing praise to the Lord with clapping
    hands.
Sing praise to the Lord with dancing feet,
sing praise to the Lord with our voice.
La, la, la, la, la, etc.

78 Unknown

God is so good,
God is so good,
God is so good,
he's so good to me.

He took my sin,
he took my sin,
he took my sin,
he's so good to me.

Now I am free,
now I am free,
now I am free,
he's so good to me.

God is so good,
he took my sin,
now I am free,
he's so good to me.

© Copyright Control

79 Capt. Alan Price, CA

God is the one who wants the best for me,
wants me to be the best that I can be.
Jesus came to show the way that I could
    know
life in all its fullness if to him I go.
He forgives my sin and fills me ev'ry day
with power to live for Jesus in all I do
    and say.
There is nothing in my life for which he
    doesn't care,
he always will be with me, all the time
    and ev'rywhere.*

Last time
He always will be with me, all the time
    and ev'rywhere;
he always will be with me, all the time
    and ev'rywhere.

© 1998 Daybreak Music Ltd

80 Unknown

God loves you, and I love you,
and that's the way it should be.
God loves you, and I love you,
and that's the way it should be.

You can be happy, and I can be happy,
and that's the way it should be.
You can be happy, and I can be happy,
and that's the way it should be.

You can be very sad, I can be very sad;
that's not the way it should be.
You can be very sad, I can be very sad;
that's not the way it should be, 'cos . . .

We can love others like sisters and
    brothers;
and that's the way it should be.
We can love others like sisters and
    brothers;
and that's the way it should be.

© Copyright Control

81 Derek Llewellyn

God loves you so much,
God wants you so much,
God wants to tell you so much
that he put it in a book for you.

And it's the Bible.
Yes, it's the Bible.
Oh, it's the Bible.
Yes, he put it in a letter
so we could know him better.

He wants to know you so much,
he wants to know you so much,
God wants to tell you so much
that he put it in a book for,
put it in a book for,
put it in a book for you.

© Sea Dream Music

82 Michael Forster

God made a boomerang and called it
  love,
God made a boomerang and called it
  love,
God made a boomerang and called it
  love,
and then he threw it away!

Love's like a boomerang, that's what
  we've found,
it comes right back when you throw it
  around.
Something we can share out,
never seems to wear out,
love's like a boomerang, let's throw it
  around.

Love's like a boomerang, that's what
  God planned,
but it's no use if it stays in your hand.
Gotta send it spinning
for a new beginning,
love's like a boomerang, let's throw it
  around.

Love's like a boomerang, goes with a
  swing,
now ev'rybody can have a good fling.
Families and nations
join the celebrations,
love's like a boomerang, let's throw it
  around.

© 1999 Kevin Mayhew Ltd

83 Capt. Alan Price, CA

God never gives up,
he never gives up,
he never gives up on me, no sir!
God never gives up,
he never gives up,
he never will cease to care!

I know I don't deserve the love
that Jesus has for me.
He died that I could be forgiv'n
and be all I could be!

Even when I forget him
and hardly ever pray,
the Spirit of Jesus deep inside
assures me when I say . . .

Even when I deny him,
pretend that I don't care,
the Spirit of Jesus deep inside
reminds me he's still there!

Even when I might hurt him
with careless words and deeds,
Father God still will love me,
and care for all my needs!
So I'll never give up,
try not to give up,
try not to give up on him, please God!
His Spirit within will help me to win
when I'm tempted to give up on him!

© 1998 Daybreak Music Ltd

84 Iain D. Craig

God's love is deeper than the deepest
  ocean,
God's love is wider than the widest sea,
God's love is higher than the highest
  mountain,
deeper, wider, higher is God's love to me.

God's grace is deeper than . . .

God's joy is deeper than . . .

God's peace is deeper than . . .

Deeper, wider, higher,
deeper, wider, higher,
deeper, wider, higher is God to me.

© 1993 Daybreak Music Ltd.

85 Unknown

God's not dead, (no), he is alive.
God's not dead, (no), he is alive.
God's not dead, (no), he is alive.
Serve him with my hands,
follow with my feet,
love him in my heart,
know him in my life;
for he's alive in me.

© 1986 Horrobin/Leavers

86 John Hardwick

God's people aren't super-brave, super-
     heroes,
they don't have muscles from their
     heads to their toes.
They're not gladiators, that's easy to see.
In fact, it's amazing, they are just like
     you and me!
(Repeat)
Sometimes scared, shaking and a-shiv'ring.
But let's realise we've got God on our side,
and he can do absolutely anything.
God's people aren't super-brave, super-
     heroes,
they don't have muscles from their
     heads to their toes.
They're not gladiators, that's easy to see.
In fact it's amazing, they are just like you
     and me!

© 1996 John Hardwick

87 Jim Bailey

God's rubbered out all my mistakes,
he's erased all my sin.
He's the ruler of creation,
no one measures up to him.
His word gets me straight to the point,
I'm sharp'ner ev'ry day;
I'm reminded of this from the contents
of my pencil case.

My pencil case, my pencil case;
I'm reminded of this from the contents
     of my pencil case.
(Repeat)

I am never stationery,
always moving on.
I felt the tip of his love,
now I know that God's right on.
His love's compassed about me,
I'm stapled to his grace;
I'm reminded of this from the contents
of my pencil case.

© 1997 Kingsway's Thankyou Music

88 Paul Crouch and David Mudie

God trains all his children
as a gardener trains a vine,
watering and pruning
so it grows into the sunshine.
And in time he is rewarded
when he sees fruit on the tree.
So our Father loves to see
the Spirit's fruit in you and me.
Love, joy, peace, patience,
goodness, kindness, faithfulness,
gentleness and self-control.

© 1997 Daybreak Music Ltd

89 Graeme Young

God, you can use me,
God, you can use me,
that the world may hear
the Lord Jesus,
God, you can use me.

. . . that the world may see . . .

. . . that the world may love . . .

God, you can use us . . .
     . . . that the world may praise . . .

© Chasah Music/Daybreak Music Ltd

90 Jim Bailey

Go, go, go into the world.
Go, go, go into the world.
Go, go, go into the world.
Tell your mum and dad
the good news that you've had;
Jesus Christ is Lord.

Go, go, go into the world.
Go, go, go into the world.
Go, go, go into the world.
Go and tell the rest
Jesus is the best;
tell every boy and girl.

© 1994 Kingsway's Thankyou Music

91 Capt. Alan Price, CA

Good or bad, right or wrong,
we have to choose each day.
Truth or lie, share or keep,
ignore the rules or obey.
Jesus is the one we need
to help us choose the right way;
Jesus, you're the one we need,
help us, Lord, today!

© 1990 Daybreak Music Ltd

92 Paul Crouch and David Mudie

Grace is when God gives us
the things we don't deserve.
Grace is when God gives us
the things we don't deserve.
He does it because he loves us,
he does it because he loves us.
Grace is when God gives us
the things we don't deserve.

Mercy is when God does not
give us what we deserve.
Mercy is when God does not
give us what we deserve.
He does it because he loves us,
he does it because he loves us.
Mercy is when God does not
give us what we deserve.

© 1989 Daybreak Music Ltd

93 Doug Horley

Hands, hands, fingers, thumbs,
we can lift to praise you.
Hands, hands, fingers, thumbs,
we can lift to praise.
Hands, hands, fingers, thumbs,
we can lift to praise you.
Jump front, jump back, yeah!
We were made to praise.*

We've got some hands that we
   can raise.
We've got a voice to shout your praise,
   Jesus!
Got some feet a-made to dance;
let's use them now we've got
   the chance.
(Repeat)

   * Last time
   We were made to praise you,
   we were made to praise.
   We were made to praise you,
   we were made to praise.

© 1996 Kingsway's Thankyou Music

94 Richard Hubbard

Hang on, stand still, stay put, hold tight;
wait for the Spirit of God.
Don't push, don't shove, don't move,
    that's right,
just wait for the Spirit of God.
(Repeat)

For you will receive the power of God.
You will receive the power of God.
You will receive the power of God
when the Holy Spirit is upon you.

Let go, launch out,
press on, don't fight;
be filled with the Spirit of God.
Move on, make way,
step out, that's right;
be filled with the Spirit of God.
(Repeat)

For you have received the power of
    God.
You have received the power of God.
You have received the power of God
now the Holy Spirit lives within you.

95 Nick Harding

Harvest time is the time when all the
    crops are high,
all the food must be cut and stored up
    in the dry.
Harvest time – see the fruit, the maize
    and wheat,
all the food for us to eat,
it must be harvest time.

Harvest time, we have always got so
    much to eat,
but for some just a little is a real feast.
Harvest time – let's remember all the
    poor,
and let's try to give them more
after this harvest time.

Harvest time is the time when we should
    all thank God
for each grain, ev'ry apple and the green
    pea pod.
Harvest time – see the fruit, the maize
    and wheat,
so much food for us to eat.
Thank God for harvest time.

96 Doug Horley

Have we made our God too small,
    too small?
Have we made our God too small?
He made the heavens and earth
and he reigns on high,
yet he's got the time for you and I.
(Repeat)

See the glory of God light up the sky,
as the clouds proclaim he reigns on
    high.
See the huge expanse of the oceans
    wide,
and a billion stars that grace the sky.
I'm awed by the power,
awed by the marks of God all around
    me,
yet humbled ev'ry day, by my
    unbelieving ways.
I really, really want it to change.

97 Mick Gisbey

Have you got an appetite?
Do you eat what is right?
Are you feeding on the word of God?
Are you fat or are you thin?
Are you really full within?
Do you find your strength in him
or are you starving?

You and me, all should be
exercising regularly,
standing strong all day long,
giving God the glory.
Feeding on the living Bread,
not eating crumbs but loaves instead;
standing stronger, living longer,
giving God the glory.

If it's milk or meat you need,
why not have a slap-up feed,
and stop looking like a weed and start
    to grow?
Take the full-of-fitness food,
taste and see that God is good,
come on, feed on what you should and
    be healthy.

98 Ralph Chambers

Have you heard about the boy in the
    multi-coloured coat?
All his brothers thought it was a great
    big joke,
but he grew up to be Prime Minister you
    see.
Joseph was on the side of God.

It's amazing what the Lord can do
through a boy or girl like me or you.
It cannot be denied that with God on
    your side,
it's amazing what the Lord can do.

Have you heard about the boy in the
    lions' den?
Punished by the king for praying to the
    Lord and then
God's angel came to save his servant
    from the grave.
Daniel was on the side of God.

Have you heard about the boy with the
    sling and the stone?
How he fought a ten-foot giant all alone.
God chose him to be king, a most
    unusual thing.
David was on the side of God.

99 Christian Strover

Have you heard the raindrops drumming
    on the rooftops?
Have you heard the raindrops dripping
    on the ground?
Have you heard the raindrops splashing
    in the streams
and running to the rivers all around?

There's water, water of life,
Jesus gives us the water of life;
there's water, water of life,
Jesus gives us the water of life.

There's a busy worker digging in the
    desert,
digging with a spade that flashes in the
    sun;
soon there will be water rising in the
    well-shaft,
spilling from the bucket as it comes.

Continued overleaf

There's water, water of life,
Jesus gives us the water of life;
there's water, water of life,
Jesus gives us the water of life.

Nobody can live who hasn't any water,
when the land is dry, then nothing much
    grows;
Jesus gives us life if we drink the living
    water,
sing it so that ev'rybody knows.

100   P. A. Taylor

Have you seen the pussy-cat sitting on
    the wall?
Have you heard his beautiful purr? (purr)
Have you seen the lion stalking round
    his prey?
Have you heard his terrible roar? (roar)

One so big, one so small,
our heav'nly Father cares for them all;
one so big, one so small,
our heav'nly Father cares.

Have you seen the children coming
    home from school?
Have you heard them shout, 'Hurray!'
    (Hurray!)
Have you seen the grown-ups coming
    home from work,
saying, 'What a horrible day!' (What a
    horrible day!)

Some so big . . .

101   O. A. Lambert

Heaven is a wonderful place,
filled with glory and grace.
I wanna see my Saviour's face.
Heaven is a wonderful place.
(I wanna go there!)

102   Iain Craig

He is the King of kings and Lord of
*   lords,*
he is the loving, living Word.
He reigns on high and yet he is my
*   friend,*
and Jesus is his name.

All my friends at school say I'm a fool
because I trust in him ev'ry day,
and I hold on to what I know is true,
he is the light, the truth, the way.

When I feel far from him, he is still there.
He draws so close as I talk to him in
    prayer.
He is my Lord and yet he is a King,
and Jesus is his name.

103   Kevin Prosch

He is the Lord, and he reigns on high;
he is the Lord.
Spoke into the darkness, created the light.
He is the Lord.
Who is like unto him, never-ending in
    days;
he is the Lord.
And he comes in power when we call on
    his name.
He is the Lord.

Show your power, O Lord our God,
show your power, O Lord our God,
*   our God.*

Your gospel, O Lord, is the hope for our
   nation;
you are the Lord.
It's the power of God for our salvation.
You are the Lord.
We ask not for riches, but look to the
   cross;
you are the Lord.
And for our inheritance give us the lost.
You are the Lord.

Send your power, O Lord our God,
send your power, O Lord our God,
*   our God.*

© 1991 Mercy/Vineyard Publishing/Music Services/CopyCare

104   Chris Jackson

Here I am, Lord,
here I am.
I'm only a child, Lord,
but here I am.

Make me like Jesus,
fill me with pow'r;
I want to serve you,
that's my desire.

© 1989 Powerpack/Learning Curve Music

105   Merete Åsebøe-Blindheim trans. Capt. Alan Price, CA

Here I am, ready to go,
excitement spreading from head to
*   toe!*
God has said he's planned a way
for me to live my life each day;
I could choose a way that's easiest
but I know that his way is the best!

Like a treasure map of old,
the Bible shows the path to follow;
Jesus said, he is the way,
sometimes it's a road that's narrow.
But the Spirit of Jesus is here, deep
   inside,
a friend always with me, my helper and
   guide!

© Daybreak Music Ltd

106   Matt Redman and Capt. Alan Price, CA

Here's a song, bursting out of my heart
   once again.
Jesus Christ, you're so good that I can't
   keep it in.
Ev'ry time I think of you, my heart
   begins to sing . . .

Listen, Lord, to the songs we sing,
   la la la, la la la;
they're a sign of the love we bring,
   la la la, la la la.

Na na na, na na na . . . (to the tune of
   'Here we go' football chant) picking
   up the song once more at
   'Listen, Lord . . .'

© 1998 Kingsway's Thankyou Music

107   Issac Balinda

Higher, higher, higher, higher, higher,
higher, higher, lift up Jesus higher.
Higher, higher, higher, higher, higher,
higher, higher, lift up Jesus higher.

Lower, lower, lower, lower, lower,
lower, lower, lower Satan lower.
Lower, lower, lower, lower, lower,
lower, lower, lower Satan lower.

Continued overleaf

Cast your burdens on to Jesus,
he cares for you.
Cast your burdens on to Jesus,
he cares for you.

Higher, higher, higher, higher, higher,
higher, higher, lift up Jesus higher.
Higher, higher, higher, higher, higher,
higher, higher, lift up Jesus higher.

108 Mark and Helen Johnson

Higher than the highest mountain,
deeper than the deepest deep blue sea,
stronger than the love of ev'ryone,
is the love of Jesus for me!

We're talkin' 'bout Jesus,
we're talkin' 'bout Jesus,
we're talkin' 'bout Jesus, Jesus,
Jesus and his love for me!

We're singin' 'bout Jesus . . .

We're whisp'rin' 'bout Jesus . . .

We're shoutin' 'bout Jesus . . .

109 Unknown

Ho ho ho hosanna,
ha ha halleluia.
He he he he loves me,
and I've got the joy of the Lord.

110 Doug Horley

Hold on to the promises of God,
hold on to the promises of God,
when it's tough and hard in your back
* yard*
you gotta hold on to the promises of
* God.*

God said to Abraham, 'Hey, you'll have
  an heir,
get offa the floor, stop laughing like a
  bear'.
Abraham said, 'But I'm way past my
  prime,
have you lost count, Lord, 'cause I'm
  eighty-five'.
God said, 'Well, that's no problem to me,
believe what is said 'cause it's meant to
  be'. You gotta

Now Abraham believed what God said
  was true,
but in case he was wrong he had plan
  number two.
And through his servant he got himself
  a son.
He thought at last the promise had
  come,
but God said, 'This is your plan, not
  mine,
I'll do it my way and in my time'.

God said to Abraham, 'Look up in the
  sky,
count all the stars way way up high.
That's the size of family I'll give to you,
if you obey what I say in all you do.
That's the good news, but now here's a
  surprise,
the bad news is, you've gotta be
  circumcised!'

So Isaac was born and Abram was
    proud,
but a voice from on high came through
    clear and loud.
This boy will be a sacrifice.
Abram said, 'Hey, that's not very nice',
but by now he knew it really paid to
    obey;
he said to Isaac, 'We're going out for the
    day'.

Tied hand and foot, on his back Isaac
    lay,
as his Dad raised the knife he knew this
    was not his day!
But with seconds to spare God stepped
    in, in time.
Isaac said, 'Phew! Well, you cut that a bit
    fine!'
God said to Abraham, 'You've passed
    the last test,
you really have proved you're the best of
    the best'.

111   Carl Tuttle

Hosanna, hosanna, hosanna in the
    highest!
Hosanna, hosanna, hosanna in the
    highest!
Lord, we lift up your name,
with hearts full of praise;
be exalted, O Lord, my God!
Hosanna in the highest!

Glory, glory, glory to the King of kings!
Glory, glory, glory to the King of kings!
Lord, we lift up your name,
with hearts full of praise;
be exalted, O Lord, my God!
Glory to the King of kings!

112   Hugh Mitchell

How did Moses cross the Red Sea?
How did Moses cross the Red Sea?
How did Moses cross the Red Sea?
How did he get across?
Did he swim? No! No!
Did he row? No! No!
Did he jump? No! No! No! No!
Did he drive? No! No!
Did he fly? No! No!
How did he get across?
God blew with his wind, puff, puff, puff,
    puff,
he blew just enough, 'nough, 'nough,
    'nough, 'nough,
and through the sea he made a path,
that's how he got across.

113   Capt. Alan Price, CA

How good of Father God
to give us gifts we don't deserve,
so many ways to demonstrate his
    power!
It's just because he loves us
and because he wants to use us.
Bring his kingdom to a world that has
    gone sour.
Holy Spirit we are ready now,
willing now to hear and to obey.
Spirit of Jesus come and touch us now,
give power for your work through us
    today.

114 Graham Kendrick

I am a lighthouse,
a shining and bright house,
out in the waves of a stormy sea.
The oil of the Spirit
keeps my lamp burning;
Jesus, my Lord, is the light in me.
And when people see
the good things that I do,
they'll give praises to God
who has sent us to Jesus.
We'll send out a lifeboat
of love and forgiveness
and give them a hand to get in.
(Repeat)
While the storm is raging, whoosh,
   whoosh,
and the wind is blowing, oo, oo,
and the waves are crashing,
crash! crash! crash! crash!
I am a lighthouse,
a shining and bright house,
out in the waves of a stormy sea.
The oil of the Spirit
keeps my lamp burning;
Jesus, my Lord, is the light in me.

115 Dave Bilbrough

I am a new creation,
no more in condemnation,
here in the grace of God I stand.
My heart is overflowing,
my love just keeps on growing,
here in the grace of God I stand.
And I will praise you, Lord,
yes, I will praise you, Lord,
and I will sing of all that you have done.
A joy that knows no limit,
a lightness in my spirit,
here in the grace of God I stand.

116 Capt. Alan Price, CA

I am a soldier in the army of the Lord,
Jesus is my commander,
I will listen and obey his ev'ry word,
I will not be a bystander.

I'll fight against the wrong I see,
including ev'ry wrong in me!
I won't let Satan get a hold,
I'll trust in Jesus and be bold!
Na na na na na na na na.

The pow'r of love and the word of the
   Lord
is like a mighty two-edged sword.
God's armour I'll put on with glee,
it's his protection over me.
Na na na na na na na na.

Breastplate of righteousness,
belt of truth, shield of faith,
hat of salvation, shoes of the gospel,
sword of the Spirit,
this your armour to put on now.

117 Jim Bailey

I am fearfully and wonderfully made.
I am fearfully and wonderfully made.
He who put the stars in place,
and knows them all by name,
has made me fearfully and wonderfully
   made.

I am made in the image of God.
I am made in the image of God.
From the top of my head
to the tips of my toes,
my Lord, my name he knows,
I am made in the image of God.

118 Capt. Alan Price, CA

I am part of God's plan,
ev'ry one of us can be too,
be part of his plan!

Jesus said his kingdom belongs
to children such as you and me!
I'll live as a child of the King,
be what he wants me to be!

His plan is to win back the world,
make it what it ought to be!
I'll fight as a child of the King,
by the power of his Spirit in me!

© 1990 Daybreak Music Ltd

119 Capt. Alan Price, CA

I am so glad, I am so very glad
that Jesus showed his love for me,
makes me the best that I can be!
I am so glad, I am so very glad
that Jesus is the best friend of all!*

He's always there whatever I do,
working, playing, sleeping too!
There's no place that I can be
where he can never care for me.
Life is such a wonderful thing,
'cos my friend is the King of kings!

* Last time
that Jesus is the best friend,
Jesus is the best friend,
Jesus is the best friend of all!

© 1998 Daybreak Music Ltd

120 Jim Bailey

I am the APPLE of God's eye,
his BANANA over me is love.
He ORANGES his angels to look after
    me,
as his blessings PLUMmet from above.

Never have to play the GOOSEBERRY,
feel like a LEMON, no not me,
for wherever this MANGOES,
a RASPBERRY it never blows.

> *The GREAT FRUIT of God,*
> *the GREAT FRUIT of God,*
> *the GREAT FRUIT of God*
> *it overflows.*
> *The GREAT FRUIT of God,*
> *the GREAT FRUIT of God,*
> *the GREAT FRUIT of God*
> *it overflows.*

I will praise him on the TANGERINE,
praise him on the MANDARIN;
SATSUMA or later you will see
there is always a CLEMENTINE for
    praising him.

© 1996 Kingsway's Thankyou Music

121 Chris Jackson

Boys	Girls
I am the way	(I am the way),
I am the truth	(I am the truth),
I am the life	(I am the life),

All: I am the way, the truth, the life.

I am the way   (I am the way),
I am the truth   (I am the truth);
All: No one comes to the Father,
no one comes to the Father but by me.

© 1991 Powerpack/Learning Curve Music

122 Marc Nelson

I believe in Jesus;
I believe he is the Son of God.
I believe he died and rose again,
I believe he paid for us all.

And I believe he's here now
(I believe that he's here),
standing in our midst;
here with the power to heal now
(with the power to heal),
and the grace to forgive.

I believe in you, Lord;
I believe you are the Son of God.
I believe you died and rose again,
I believe you paid for us all.

And I believe you're here now
(I believe that you're here),
standing in our midst;
here with the power to heal now
(with the power to heal),
and the grace to forgive.

123 Capt. Alan Price, CA

I can be what God wants me to be,
let the fruit of the Spirit grow in me.
More like Jesus I would be;
Holy Spirit, work in me,
Holy Spirit, work in me.

I can do what God wants me to do,
by the power of the Spirit too,
there are things he's planned for me to
    do;
Holy Spirit, work in me,
Holy Spirit, work in me.

124 Jim Bailey

I can do all, (all!) all, (all!) all things
through Christ who strengthens me.
I can do all, (all!) all, (all!) all things
through Christ who strengthens me.

Go to school: all things.
Obey the rules: all things.
Keep my cool: all things,
through Christ who strengthens me.

Make new friends: all things.
Give and lend: all things.
Make amends: all things,
through Christ who strengthens me.

Pray and sing: all things.
Love our King: all things.
Ev'rything: all things,
through Christ who strengthens me.

125 Martin Smith

Oh, I could sing unending songs
of how you saved my soul.
Well, I could dance a thousand miles
because of your great love.

My heart is bursting, Lord,
to tell of all you've done.
Of how you changed my life
and wiped away the past.
I wanna shout it out,
from ev'ry roof-top sing.
For now I know that God
is for me, not against me.

Ev'rybody's singing now,
'cos we're so happy!
Ev'rybody's dancing now,
'cos we're so happy!
If only we could see your face
and see you smiling over us
and unseen angels celebrate,
for joy is in this place.

126 Mike Burn

I'd reach for the stars,
climb the highest mountain,
run a million miles,
swim the widest sea,
jump over the moon,
that's how much I love you,
I'd do anything for you, my Lord.

What can I say? what can I do?
to show you, Jesus, that I love you.
I give you my heart, I give you my song,
O, Jesus, I want you to know . . .

What do you ask? what should I do?
Please help me, Jesus, to follow you.
I give you my life, I give you my will,
O, Jesus, I want you to know . . .

127 Mike Burn

If I look in a mirror and there I see my face,
but forget what I look like as soon as I
    walk away,
that is what it's like if I hear God's word
and I'm foolish enough not to obey.
'Cos happy are those who hear the word
    of God,
happy are those who trust it and obey.
No other way to find true happiness
than to hear the word of God and obey.

128 Brian Howard

If I were a butterfly,
I'd thank you, Lord, for giving me
    wings,
and if I were a robin in a tree,
I'd thank you, Lord, that I could sing,
and if I were a fish in the sea,
I'd wiggle my tail and I'd giggle with
    glee;
but I just thank you, Father, for making
    me 'me'.

For you gave me a heart,
and you gave me a smile,
you gave me Jesus
and you made me your child,
and I just thank you, Father,
for making me 'me'.

If I were an elephant,
I'd thank you, Lord, by raising my
    trunk,
and if I were a kangaroo,
you know I'd hop right up to you,
and if I were an octopus,
I'd thank you, Lord, for my fine looks;
but I just thank you, Father, for making
    me 'me'.

If I were a wiggly worm,
I'd thank you, Lord, that I could squirm,
and if I were a billy goat,
I'd thank you, Lord, for my strong
    throat,
and if I were a fuzzy wuzzy bear,
I'd thank you, Lord, for my fuzzy wuzzy
    hair;
but I just thank you, Lord, for making
    me 'me'.

129 Sammy Horner

If Jesus is de vine, we must be de
branches.
If Jesus is de vine, we must be de
branches.
If Jesus is de vine, we must be de
branches,
and bear fruit in the kingdom of God.

If Jesus is de rock, we should be a little
bolder.
If Jesus is de rock, we should be a little
bolder.
If Jesus is de rock, we should be a little
bolder,
to bear fruit in the kingdom of God.

If Jesus is de bread, is your name on the
roll now?
If Jesus is de bread, is your name on the
roll now?
If Jesus is de bread, is your name on the
roll now,
to bear fruit in the kingdom of God?

130 Kath Fathers

If we admit to God that we've done
wrong
(I'm really sorry, Lord),
he says he will forgive us
and he will keep his promise
and he will make us clean on the
inside.
(Repeat)
All his promises are true,
let him make them true for you.
All his promises are true,
let him make them true for you.

131 Sammy Horner

If you feel unhappy or you're feeling sad,
don't hide your tears, don't hide your
tears,
'cause I know of someone who won't
treat you bad,
Jesus loves even you.

Jesus loves even you, friend,
Jesus loves even you.
He's promised to dry
ev'ry tear from your eye,
Jesus loves even you.

If you want to cry when you watch your
TV,
don't hold it back, don't hold it back,
for Jesus cries too for those children you
see,
Jesus loves even you.

Tonight when you go to your bedroom
to sleep,
don't be afraid, don't be afraid,
for Jesus has promised our souls he will
keep,
Jesus loves even you.

132 Ian White

If you're going to run the race and win,
you've got to know where to begin.
You need to learn about the Lord,
and start by reading his Word.

Reading his Word, Genesis and Exodus.
Reading his Word, Leviticus and
Numbers.
Reading his Word, Deuteronomy, Joshua
and Judges.
Reading his Word, Ruth, Samuel and
Kings.

Reading his Word, Chronicles and Ezra.
Reading his Word, Nehemiah and Esther.
Reading his Word, Job, Psalms and
    Proverbs.
Reading his Word, Ecclesiastes and Song
    of Solomon.

Reading his Word, Isaiah and Jeremiah.
Reading his Word, Lamentations and
    Ezekiel.
Reading his Word, Daniel and Hosea.
Reading his Word, Joel and Amos.

Reading his Word, Obadiah and Jonah.
Reading his Word, Micah and Nahum.
Reading his Word, Habakkuk and
    Zephaniah.
Reading his Word, Haggai, Zechariah
    and Malachi.

Reading his Word, Matthew, Mark, Luke
    and John.
Reading his Word, Acts, Romans and
    Corinthians.
Reading his Word, Galatians, Ephesians
    and Philippians.
Reading his Word, Colossians,
    Thessalonians and Timothy.

Reading his Word, Titus and Philemon.
Reading his Word, Hebrews and James.
Reading his Word, the letters of Peter
    and John.
Reading his Word, Jude and Revelation.

133 Richard Hubbard

If your output exceeds your input,
your upkeep will be your downfall.
But if your input exceeds your output,
you can hold your head up
and push the enemy down.

134 Peter and Hanneke Jacobs

If you see a special way
to give the Lord's great love away,
you don't have to wait till you're grown
    up,
'cos God can use you now.
If you want to tell someone
the special things that the Lord has
    done,
you don't have to wait,
'cos God can use you now!

God uses kids
who open up their hearts to him
and let his love flow through them,
God uses kids!
God uses kids
to share his joy in many ways,
and as we give his love each day,
God uses kids!

I can pray for God to bring
people that I love to him,
I don't have to wait till I'm grown up,
'cos God can use me now.
I can pray with others who
want to know God's healing too,
I don't have to wait,
'cos God can use me now!

135 Mick Gisbey

I have hidden your word in my heart,
that I might not sin against you.
I have hidden your word in my heart,
that I might not sin against you,
that I might not sin against you,
that I might not sin against you.
I have hidden your word in my heart,
that I might not sin against you.

136 Paul Field

I just want to thank you, Lord,
for all the things you give,
for all my family and my friends,
for the good life that we live.

Help me learn to look to you,
and care for others more.
Help me trust in you each day,
whenever I'm unsure.

You will be my guiding light,
you will lead me through my life,
even in the darkest night,
you shine for me.
Through my doubts and through my
*   fears,*
through the laughter and the tears,
through the passing of the years,
you'll always be my guiding light.

Lead me always in your steps,
beautiful and true.
Jesus, you will light the way,
and I will follow you.

137 Capt. Alan Price, CA

I love the lights on the Christmas trees,
I love the carols we sing,
I love the magic of Christmas time,
but most of all I love Jesus, my King.
We celebrate the birthday of Jesus,
    God's son,
who left the glory of heaven
and was born a baby in Bethlehem.
A tiny baby like ev'ryone *(first time)*
(Repeat)

A human baby like ev'ryone *(second time)*

I love the lights on the Christmas trees,
I love the carols we sing,
I love the magic of Christmas time,
but most of all I love Jesus, my King.

138 Mike Burn

I love to be with you, Jesus,
listening to your voice,
and when I hear you speak my name,
my heart and soul rejoice,
and if you said 'jump',
I'd jump for joy,
and if you said 'run',
I'd run to your side,
and if you said 'leap',
I'd take a leap of faith,
and if you said 'dance',
I'd dance for sheer delight.

To be with you, to be with you,
to be with you, oh, it's the best thing.
To be with you, to be with you,
to be with you, it's the best thing in
*   my life.*

139 David Mudie and Paul Crouch

I love you, Lord Jesus,
the King of all things.
You love me, Lord Jesus,
your love never ends.
To you I am special,
your promises are true.
You love me, Lord Jesus,
and Lord, I love you.

140 Rob Hayward

I'm accepted, I'm forgiven,
I am fathered by the true and living God.
I'm accepted, no condemnation,
I am loved by the true and living God.
There's no guilt or fear as I draw near
to the Saviour and Creator of the world.
There is joy and peace as I release
my worship to you, O Lord.

I may be small, but I'm powerful,
God has made me that way,
recharged by the Holy Spirit
ev'ry day.

Being connected to Jesus
lights me on my way,
giving me the power
to live each day.

141 Capt. Alan Price, CA

I'm a full-time Christian,
working for the Lord,
I'm trying to honour Jesus, not seeking a
    reward.
Whatever I do, I do for him,
and try my best, you see,
so glory goes to Father God,
and not just to me.

I'll work for Jesus, whatever I do,
I'll work for Jesus, why don't you?
I'll work for Jesus, come what may,
I'll work for Jesus ev'ry day!

I'm a full-time Christian,
whatever I may be,
playing, working, or at home,
    watching the TV.
I'll make mistakes, I'll get things wrong,
but I will try and see
that glory goes to Father God
and isn't spoilt by me.

142 Ron Sivers

I'm a pow pow pow pow pow pow
pow powerpack!
I'm a pow pow pow pow pow pow
pow powerpack!

143 Ron Sivers

I'm a winner when I run with Jesus,
I'm a winner when I go his way.
A crown of everlasting joy
will be mine one day.
I'm blessed when I'm faithful to Jesus,
I'm blessed by his promise to me;
because of him I'm heaven-bound,
a winner I will be, a winner you will see,
a winner in Jesus, that's me!

144 Ian Smale

I may live in a great big city,
I may live in a village small,
I may live in a tiny house,
I may live in a tower tall,
I may live in the countryside,
I may live by the sea,
but wherever I live, I know
that Jesus also lives with me,
but wherever I live, I know
Jesus lives with me.

145 Capt. Alan Price, CA

I'm enthusiastic, boing, boing, boing!
I think it's fantastic, yeah, yeah, yeah!
I'm enthusiastic, boing, boing, boing!
I think it's fantastic, yeah, yeah, yeah!

Jesus showed just how much God loves
  me (you and me!)
That is why I follow him you see,
do you see, do you see, do you see?

I'm gonna work and do what I can do.
Read my Bible, pray and worship too,
yes I will, yes I will, yes I will!

146 Jim Bailey

I'm getting to know God as my Dad,
I'm getting to know God as my Father;
it's mega, yeah! to know he loves and
  cares,
yes, I'm getting to know I've a Dad
  upstairs.

Dads are often busy with important
  things to do,
but a Father in heaven always has time
  for you.
Dads are very special but sometimes not
  around,
but a Father in heaven always can be
  found.

147 Christopher Jackson

I'm gonna be a mighty warrior,
I'm gonna be a mighty warrior,
filled with your Holy Spirit,
filled with power and might.

Oh! mighty warrior,
raising up a banner,
fighting for what's right,
lifting up your name in all the earth.
Though I find it hard, Lord,
I'll try with all my might,
'cos I want to see
your Kingdom come in power.
I'm gonna be a mighty warrior,
I'm gonna be a mighty warrior,
filled with your Holy Spirit,
filled with power and might.
Oh! mighty warrior!
Oh! mighty warrior!

148 Doug Horley

I'm gonna build my house on solid
  rock,
I'm gonna build my house on solid
  rock,
so I don't wake up to a nasty shock,
to find nothing but a pile of rubble.

Don't want to build a house on
  foundations that will wobble.
Don't want to build a house with any
  dodgy bricks.
Don't want to build a house that will
  shake like a jelly.
I want to shout out loud, of this house
  you can be proud!

Jesus said, 'Take my words and put them
  into action;
make these words', he said, 'foundations
  in your life.
Build with care or else your house will
  surely tumble,
and it's not a clever trick to own a heap
  of bricks.'

Jesus said, 'Take my words and put them
    into action;
make these words', he said, 'foundations
    in your life.
And when the river comes and crashes
    up against you,
you won't get washed away, instead
    you'll cheer and say:

Yes, I built my house on solid rock,
yes, I built my house on solid rock,
and I won't wake up to a nasty shock,
to find nothing but a pile of rubble.'

149   John Fryer

I'm gonna clap my hands and shout
    out loud,
I'm gonna raise my voice above the
    crowd,
because Jesus is the one for me.
I'm gonna dance and cheer and stamp
    my feet,
I'm gonna sing this song walking
    down the street,
because Jesus is the one for me.
(Repeat)

J and E and S - U - S;
He's the King and I must say 'Yes!'
Jesus is the one for me!
J and E and S - U - S;
no one else, no second best.
Jesus is the one for me.

150   Capt. Alan Price, CA

I'm gonna click, click, click,
I'm gonna clap, clap, clap,
I'm gonna click, I'm gonna clap
and praise the Lord!

Because of all he's done
I'm gonna make him 'number one',
I'm gonna click, I'm gonna clap
and praise the Lord!

I'm gonna zoom, zoom, zoom,
around the room, room, room,
I'm gonna zoom around the room
and praise the Lord!
Because of all he's done,
I'm gonna make him 'number one',
I'm gonna zoom around the room
and praise the Lord!

I'm gonna sing, sing, sing,
I'm gonna shout, shout, shout,
I'm gonna sing, I'm gonna shout
and praise the Lord!
Because of all he's done,
I'm gonna make him 'number one',
I'm gonna sing, I'm gonna shout
and praise the Lord!

I'm gonna click, click, click,
I'm gonna clap, clap, clap,
I'm gonna zoom around the room
and praise the Lord!
Because of all he's done,
I'm gonna make him 'number one',
I'm gonna sing, I'm gonna shout
and praise the Lord!

151   Mike Burn

I'm gonna dance on the streets,
I'm gonna sing in the rain,
for the Spirit of God is poured out
    again.
I'm gonna shout it aloud,
I'm gonna let the world know
that the river of God has started to flow.

Continued overleaf

And we sing Jesus, Jesus, come!
Oh, we will lift your name on high.
You are the Son of God, saving one,
Jesus, Jesus, come!

152 Capt. Alan Price, CA

I'm gonna shine, shine, shine,
a light in the world I'll be.
I want to shine, shine, shine,
let people see Jesus in me!

I want to glorify the Father
by the things I do;
be the person God has made me,
letting his love flow through!

And when it's hard 'n' it's not so easy
to know and do what's right;
I'll trust the Holy Spirit in me,
to help me win each fight.

Even if I fail him often
and my light is dim;
he has promised to forgive me,
I can come back to him!

153 Jim Bailey

I'm gonna walk by faith, not by sight;
I'm gonna walk by faith, not by sight.
I'm gonna follow Jesus, and do what's
right;
I'm gonna walk by faith, not by sight.

Jesus said, 'If you follow me,
you will never live in darkness.'
Jesus said, 'If you follow me,
you will live in the light.'
(Repeat)

I'm gonna watch and pray every day;
I'm gonna watch and pray every day.
I'm gonna do ev'rything that I heard
Jesus say.
I'm gonna watch and pray every day.

Jesus said . . .

I'm gonna watch and pray . . .

154 Capt. Alan Price, CA

I'm in-right, out-right, up-right,
down-right happy thru' and thru',
I'm in-right, out-right, up-right,
down-right happy 'cos it's true:
Jesus cared for me when he died on
    Calvary,
I'm in-right, out-right, up-right,
down-right happy thru' and thru'!

155 Ian White

I'm just a shepherd, David is my name,
I live in a village called Bethlehem.
My brothers are soldiers
and they're fighting in the war,
but I don't understand what the fighting
    is for!
I don't understand what the fighting is
    for!

I go to see my brothers
and I bring them cheese and bread,
I see Goliath and I hear the things he
    says,
he's big and mean and ugly, he's a very
    wicked man,
but I'm gonna get him if I can!
I'm gonna get him if I can!

Well, who's gonna win, tell me,
how's it gonna be?
Is it gonna be him, or is it gonna be
me?
I'm not very tall and I'm not very wide,
but I've got the fire of the Lord inside!
I've got the fire of the Lord inside!

Well, I don't need spears,
I don't need armour plate,
if the Lord will deliver me, he'll do it
anyway.
I'd rather use something that I know,
I take a little stone and here I go!
I take a little stone and here I go!

Well, Goliath, you can fight me
with your spear and with your sword,
but I come against you in the name of
the Lord!
And ev'ryone who gathers here will
understand
the battle is the Lord's and it's in our
hands,
the battle is the Lord's and it's in our
hands!

156 Mike Burn

I'm putting God's armour on,
I'm putting God's armour on,
so I can stand in his might,
fight for what is right
and walk in the light of the Lord.
(Repeat)
I put on the breastplate of
righteousness,
put truth around my waist like a belt,
I put on the shoes to announce good
news,
good news of peace in all the earth.

I lift high the shield of faith
to put out the arrows of the enemy,
put salvation on my head like a helmet.
I pick up the sword of the Spirit,
which is the word of the Lord.

157 Ian Smale

I'm putting God's gear on and I am
feeling strong,
because I know the Lord is never wrong.
For he has made it clear that he is
always near,
and his perfect love gets rid of fear.
So as I run the race at Jesus' pace,
at the finishing line there'll be no
disgrace.
Lord, I love you, and you love me too,
what a team we make.

158 Steve Bradshaw

I'm putting my hand in your hand now,
O Jesus, I ask of you,
let your Spirit flow right through my
heart.
I'm putting my hand in your hand now,
O Jesus, I ask of you,
let your Spirit flow right through my
heart.
Heal me, Lord, touch me, Lord,
let your Spirit flow right through my
heart.
Heal me, Lord, touch me, Lord,
let your Spirit flow right through my
heart.

159 Mike Burn

I'm singing your praise, Lord,
I'm singing your praise,
to show the world that I love you, Jesus,
I'm singing your praise.

So many ways, Lord,
so much that I can do
to lift your name in all the earth
to show that I love you.

I'm clapping my hands . . .

I'm shouting your name . . .

I'm jumping for joy . . .

160 Audrey Traynor

I'm so excited, Lord, I can't keep still;
I've got to jump up and down on my
feet,
'cos when I think about the way that you
love me, Lord,
I know I can't just sit in my seat, no.

Ooh, it starts in my heart now,
then it flows through my body.
Ooh, this feeling inside me, I know
that it's you.
I just can't hide it; got to let it show
now, yeah, yeah.
Jumping up and down, woa,
dancing with Jesus,
and I'm spinning round and round,
woa,
dancing with Jesus now.
I clap my hands to show, woa,
I love you, Jesus,
and I raise my arms to show, woa,
I love you, Jesus, now.

Just being here with you is oh so precious,
it's a feeling I will never forget,
and now I feel your Spirit moving within
me,
Lord, I thank you for this moment we
share, yeah.

161 Capt. Alan Price, CA

I'm sorry for the wrong I've done,
I'm sorry for the wrong I've done;
please forgive me, Lord,
please forgive me, Lord,
I'm sorry for the wrong I've done.

I'm sorry for the wrong I've said,
I'm sorry for the wrong I've said;
please forgive me, Lord,
please forgive me, Lord,
I'm sorry for the wrong I've said.

I'm sorry for the wrong I've thought,
I'm sorry for the wrong I've thought;
please forgive me, Lord,
please forgive me, Lord,
I'm sorry for the wrong I've thought.

Thank you for forgiving me,
thank you for forgiving me;
thank you, thank you, Lord,
thank you, thank you, Lord,
thank you for forgiving me!

162 Graham Kendrick

I'm special because God has loved me,
for he gave the best thing that he had
to save me;
his own Son, Jesus, crucified to take the
blame,
for all the bad things I have done.

Thank you, Jesus, thank you, Lord,
for loving me so much.
I know I don't deserve anything;
help me feel your love right now
to know deep in my heart
that I'm your special friend.

163 Ian Smale

I'm taking on board what God is saying,
I'm taking on board what God is doing,
I'm taking on board what God's
    revealing in his word.
I'm taking on board what God is saying,
I'm taking on board what God is doing,
I'm taking on board what God's
    revealing by his Spirit.

We're taking on board . . .

164 Jim Bailey

I'm working out what it means to follow
    Jesus,
adding up what it costs to follow him;
counting the times that his love is
    multiplying,
realising he took away my sin.
He's always in my memory,
he'll never cancel what he's done
    for me.
When I add it together I calculate
Jesus is great, Jesus is great!

165 Richard Hubbard

I'm your child and you are my God.
I thank you, Father, for your loving care.
I'm your child and you are my God.
You've made me special and you're
    always there.

I'm your child and you are my God.
I love you, Jesus, you're close to me.
I'm your child and you are my God.
I give you worship, I bow the knee.

I'm your child and you are my God.
Holy Spirit, flow out to me.
I'm your child and you are my God.
You give me power and authority.

166 Capt. Alan Price, CA

In all the galaxy there is no one else like
    me,
I'm a unique part of Father God's
    creation.
Sometimes weak and sometimes strong,
doing right or doing wrong,
God loves this unique part of his
    creation.
No matter how I feel about myself,
I'm the object of God's care;
he sent his son that I might know his love
all the time and ev'rywhere!
In all the galaxy there is no one else like
    me,
I'm a unique part of Father God's
    creation.
Sometimes weak and sometimes strong,
doing right or doing wrong,
God loves this unique part of his
    creation.

167 Capt. Alan Price, CA

In days of old when knights were bold
and kings ruled the land,
ev'ryone knew just what to do when
they gave a command.
Some kings ruled with kindness, and
others were so mean,
but we have a King named Jesus, the
best there's ever been!
Jesus, the King of kings, he's the King of
love,
Jesus, the King of kings, Lord of heav'n
above,
Jesus, the King of kings, royal majesty,
and his kingdom is in me.

© 1994 Daybreak Music Ltd

168 Sammy Horner

I need faith just to live my life the way I
know I should,
I need faith just to be the way the Lord
says that I could.
I need faith, faith, faith, faith,
faith ev'ry second of my life.

I need faith if I'm gonna hear the words
you say to me,
I need faith if I'm gonna be what you
want me to be.
I need faith, faith, faith, faith,
faith ev'ry second of my life.

I need faith 'cause I really want to see
your kingdom come,
I need faith just to know where all my
strength is coming from.
I need faith, faith, faith, faith,
faith ev'ry second of my life.

© 1996 Daybreak Music Ltd

169 Ian White

In ev'rything that I do, show me what
Jesus would do.
In ev'rything that I do, show me what
Jesus would do.
I will not be afraid, for I can always pray;
show me what Jesus would do.

© 1987 Little Misty Music/Kingsway's Thankyou Music

170 Ian Smale

I once was frightened of spiders,
I once was frightened of the dark;
I once was frightened by many, many
things,
especially things that barked.
But now I'm asking Jesus to help these
fears to go,
'cause I don't want them to be part of
me,
no, no, no, no, no.

I once was frightened by thunder,
and frightened of lightning too;
I once was frightened by many, many
things,
that crashed and banged and blew.
But now I'm asking Jesus,
to help these fears to go,
'cause I don't want them to be part
of me,
no, no, no, no, no.

© 1994 Kingsway's Thankyou Music

171 Judy Bailey

I reach up high, I touch the ground,
I stomp my feet and turn around.
I've got to (woo woo) praise the Lord.
I jump and dance with all my might,
I might look funny but that's all right.
I've got to (woo woo) praise the Lord.

I'll do anything just for my God,
'cos he's done ev'rything for me.
It doesn't matter who is looking on,
Jesus is the person that I want to please.

May my whole life be a song of praise,
to worship God in ev'ry way.
In this song the actions praise his name,
I want my actions ev'ry day to do the same.

172 Capt. Alan Price, CA

Is it spooky, is it weird,
that God wants to talk to you and me?
Is it something to be feared?
No! God wants the best for you and me!

He speaks through words in the Bible,
through other Christians too;
and shows us the right way we should live,
in what we say and do. Oh,

But through the Holy Spirit,
supernaturally,
he gives us words and pictures,
a gift of prophecy. Oh,

So we should learn to listen
to all that God would say,
and act on what we think he's said,
listen and obey. Oh,

173 Capt. Alan Price, CA

Isn't it good to be together,
being with friends old and new?
Isn't it good?
The Bible tells us Jesus, our Lord,
    is here too!
Isn't it good to be together,
being with friends old and new?

Isn't it good?
The Bible tells us Jesus, our Lord,
    is here too!
He's here! By his Spirit he's with us,
    he's here!
His promise is true, he's here!
Though we can't see him, he's here for
    me and for you!
He's here! By his Spirit he's with us,
    he's here!
His promise is true, he's here!
Though we can't see him, he's here for
    me and for you!

174 Capt. Alan Price, CA

It's an adventure following Jesus,
it's an adventure learning of him.
It's an adventure living for Jesus,
it's an adventure following him.
Let's go where he leads us,
turn away from wrong;
for we know we can trust him
to help us as we go along.
It's an adventure following Jesus,
it's an adventure learning of him.
It's an adventure living for Jesus,
it's an adventure following him.

175 Capt. Alan Price, CA

It's great, great, coming along;
it's great, great, great to belong;
it's great to know we're not wrong;
it's great that Jesus loves us!
It's great, great, great to be here;
it's great, great, knowing he's near;
it's great ev'rybody can hear;
it's great that Jesus loves us!
It's great that Jesus loves us!

176 Ian White

It takes an almighty hand,
to make your harvest grow;
it takes an almighty hand,
however you may sow.
It takes an almighty hand,
the world around me shows;
it takes the almighty hand of God.

It takes his hand to grow your garden,
all from a secret in a seed;
part of a plan he spoke and started,
and said is 'very good indeed'.

It takes his hand to turn the seasons,
to give the sun and snow their hour;
and in this plan we learn his reason,
his nature and eternal power.

It took his hands to carry sorrow,
for ev'ry sin that we have done;
and on a cross he bought tomorrow,
a world of good, like he'd begun.

And in his hands there is perfection,
that in this land we only taste;
for now, we see a poor reflection,
then, we shall see him face to face.

177 Chris Falson

I walk by faith, each step by faith,
to live by faith, I put my trust in you.
(Repeat)
Ev'ry step I take is a step of faith;
no weapon formed against me shall
     prosper,
and ev'ry prayer I make is a prayer of faith;
and if my God is for me,
then who can be against me?

178 Nigel Hemming

I wanna be a light in the world,
I wanna be a light in the world,
shining through the darkness so
     ev'ryone can see.
I wanna be a light in the world,
I wanna be a light in the world,
and nothing, Lord, can ever hide your
     precious love in me.

There is no secret in my eyes,
there is no need to run or hide.
I'm not afraid to tell my friends
of your love that never ends.

You take away all my fear,
you fill me with your love.
You give me strength so I can sing,
songs of praise to my King.

179 Sammy Horner

I wanna tell you how much I love you.
I wanna tell you how much I care.

Heavenly Father, we are your children,
when we need you, you'll be there.

We wanna tell you how much we love you.
We wanna tell you how much we care.

Heavenly Father, we are your children,
when we need you, you'll be there.

180 Doug Horley

I want to be a tree that's bearing fruit,
that God has pruned and caused to
     shoot,
Oh, up in the sky, so very, very high.
I want to be, I want to be a blooming tree.

God has promised his Holy Spirit
will water our roots and help us grow.
Listen and obey, and before you know it
your fruit will start to grow, grow, grow,
    grow, grow.

You'll be a tree that's bearing fruit,
with a very, very, very strong root,
bright colours like daisies, more fruit
    than Sainsbury's,
you'll be a blooming tree.

© 1996 Kingsway's Thankyou Music

181   Claire Morgans

I want to be like Jesus,
I want to love like Jesus,
I want to listen to his word.
I want to care like he does,
I want to share like he does,
I want to be a child of God.

Make me more, make me more like Jesus.
More, make me more like Jesus.

I want to be like Jesus,
I want to see like Jesus,
I want to feel the Father's heart.
I want to reach like he does
    with love to each like he does,
I want to be a child of God.

© 1997 Kingsway's Thankyou Music

182   Capt. Alan Price, CA

I want to be salt for Jesus,
salt in the world for him,
spreading the flavour of Jesus,
stirring his goodness in.
I've got the taste of Jesus,
I know what he can do!
I want to be salt for Jesus,
so you can know him too.

© 1991 Daybreak Music Ltd

183   Chris Jackson

I want to worship you all of my life,
give you praise.
I want to serve only you all of my life,
all my days.
For you are a mighty, awesome God,
and you reign in pow'r and you reign in
    love.
O Lord, you are God.

© 1998 Powerpack/Learning Curve Music

184   Matt Redman

I will dance, I will sing,
to be mad for my King.
Nothing, Lord, is hindering
the passion in my soul.
(Repeat)

And I'll become
even more undignified than this.
I'll become
even more undignified than this.
Na, na, na, na, na, na! Hey!
Na, na, na, na, na, na! Hey!
(Repeat)

© 1995 Kingsway's Thankyou Music

185   Leona von Brethorst

I will enter his gates with thanksgiving
    in my heart,
I will enter his courts with praise,
I will say this is the day that the Lord
    has made,
I will rejoice for he has made me glad.
He has made me glad,
he has made me glad,
I will rejoice for he has made me glad.
He has made me glad,
he has made me glad,
I will rejoice for he has made me glad.

© 1976 Maranatha! Music/CopyCare

186 Matt Redman

I will offer up my life
in spirit and truth,
pouring out the oil of love
as my worship to you.
In surrender I must give
my ev'ry part;
Lord, receive the sacrifice
of a broken heart.

Jesus, what can I give,
what can I bring
to so faithful a friend,
to so loving a King?
Saviour, what can be said,
what can be sung
as a praise of your name
for the things you have done?
Oh, my words could not tell,
not even in part,
of the debt of love that is owed
by this thankful heart.

You deserve my ev'ry breath
for you've paid the great cost;
giving up your life to death,
even death on a cross.
You took all my shame away,
there defeated my sin,
opened up the gates of heav'n,
and have beckoned me in.

187 Chris Jackson

I will show you my faith by my actions,
I will show you my faith by the things I
    do.
I will show you my faith by my actions.
I will glorify you.

I want my life to make a difference,
I want to tell of your great love,
to share my faith with others,
to do what you would do.
Oh, I want to be a help to you, Lord.

188 Ian Smale

I will wave my hands
in praise and adoration,
I will wave my hands
in praise and adoration,
I will wave my hands
in praise and adoration,
praise and adoration to the living God.

For he's given me hands
that just love clapping;
one, two, one, two, three,
and he's given me a voice
that just loves shouting
'Hallelujah!'
He's given me feet
that just love dancing;
one, two, one, two, three,
and he's put me in a being
that has no trouble seeing
that whatever I am feeling
he is worthy to be praised.

189 Ian Smale

I won't wander off in the darkness,
I don't want to live in the cold.
I'm not going to live like a little sheep,
who's strayed away from the fold.
I'll try and obey the good Shepherd,
as I'm one of his family.
I'm staying close to Jesus
'cos that's the very best place for me to be,
that's the very best place to be.

190 Ian Smale

Jehovah Jireh, God will provide,
Jehovah Rophe, God heals;
Jehovah M'keddesh, God who sanctifies,
Jehovah Nissi, God is my banner.

Jehovah Rohi, God my shepherd,
Jehovah Shalom, God is peace;
Jehovah Tsidkenu, God our
    righteousness,
Jehovah Shammah, God who is there.

© 1987 Kingsway's Thankyou Music

191 Capt. Alan Price, CA

Jesus came proclaiming God's kingdom
    was at hand,
for all who would believe in him,
    obeying his command;
and now he sends his deputies like you
    and me today,
to share God's love in ev'rything we do
    and what we say.

I've got my badge inside,
I'm a deputy for Jesus,
by the Holy Spirit I am marked and
    kept for God.
I'll wear my badge with pride,
I'm a deputy for Jesus,
under his authority to live and work
    for God!

Set captives free from Satan's grip, pray
    for the sick as well,
wherever you may find yourself, the
    Good News you must tell!
As Jesus sent disciples then, he sends
    us out today,
as deputies for Jesus we'll follow and
    obey.

© 1992 Daybreak Music Ltd

192 Matt Redman

Jesus Christ, I think upon your sacrifice;
you became nothing, poured out to
    death.
Many times I've wondered at your gift of
    life,
and I'm in that place once again,
I'm in that place once again.

And once again I look upon
the cross where you died.
I'm humbled by your mercy
and I'm broken inside.
Once again I thank you,
once again I pour out my life.

Now you are exalted to the highest
    place,
King of the heavens, where one day I'll
    bow.
But for now I marvel at this saving
    grace,
and I'm full of praise once again,
I'm full of praise once again.

Thank you for the cross, thank you for
    the cross,
thank you for the cross, my friend.
Thank you for the cross, thank you for
    the cross,
thank you for the cross, my friend.

© 1995 Kingsway's Thankyou Music

193 Steve Israel and Gerrit Gustafson

Jesus Christ is the Lord of all,
Lord of all the earth.
Jesus Christ is the Lord of all,
Lord of all the earth.
(Repeat)

Continued overleaf

Only one God,
over the nations,
only one Lord of all;
in no other name
is there salvation,
Jesus is Lord of all.

Jesus Christ is the Lord of all,
Lord of all the earth.
Jesus Christ is the Lord of all,
Lord of all the earth.

Jesus Christ is Lord of all,
Jesus Christ is Lord of all.
Jesus Christ is Lord of all,
Jesus Christ is Lord of all.

194   Margaret Cropper,
adapt. Stephen Hopkinson

Jesus' hands were kind hands doing
   good to all,
healing pain and sickness, blessing
   children small,
and my hands should serve him, ready
   at his call.
Jesus' hands were kind hands doing
   good to all.

195   Paul Mazak

Jesus is a friend of mine, praise him.
Jesus is a friend of mine, praise him.
Praise him, praise him.
Jesus is a friend of mine, praise him.

Jesus died to set us free, praise him . . .

He gave us the victory, praise him . . .

Jesus is the King of kings, praise him . . .

196   Gill Hutchinson

Jesus is greater than the greatest
   heroes,
Jesus is closer than the closest friends.
He came from heaven and he died to
   save us,
to show us love that never ends.
(Repeat)

Son of God, and the Lord of glory,
he's the light, follow in his way.
He's the truth, that we can believe in,
and he's the life, he's living today.
(Repeat)

197   Julia Plaut

Jesus is my friend and I'm a friend
   of Jesus.
Jesus is my friend and I'm a friend
   of his.
I can talk to him any time I like.
He's always listening,
that's how I know that Jesus is my friend
and I'm a friend of his.

198   Capt. Alan Price, CA

Jesus isn't dead any more,
that is why we sing.
Jesus isn't dead any more,
he's alive and he's the King of
   heaven.

Killed on a cross and sealed in a tomb,
but that was not the end;
God brought Jesus back to life,
now he's our living friend.

He went back to be with God,
but we know he's still near;
Jesus sent the Spirit of God,
and he is always here with us.

Jesus isn't dead any more,
that is why we sing;
Jesus isn't dead any more,
he's alive, and he's our King.

Here in my weakness, his strength is so
    clear,
thank you, Lord Jesus, you're mighty, yet
    here.
I praise you for taking all of my fear.
Help me to trust you and know you are
    near;
help me to trust you and know you are
    near.

199 Sammy Horner

Jesus is our shepherd, we must be his
    sheep,
he said that he'd protect us and give us
    food to eat,
and if a wolf comes close to us
    a shepherd makes him flee,
I don't mind being in his flock, it doesn't
    sound baa'd to me.
It doesn't sound baa'd to me.
It doesn't sound baa'd to me.
Well, I don't mind being in his flock,
it doesn't sound baa'd to me.

200 Sarah Clark

Jesus is special, special to me,
he gave his life so I could be free.
He is my friend who never leaves me.
He is so special, special to me;
he is so special, special to me.

Jesus forgave me for all of my wrong,
came to the earth so we could belong
in his kingdom, close to his heart,
Making me special, he set me apart;
making me special, he set me apart.

201 Capt. Alan Price, CA

Jesus is the lighthouse, shining all
    around,
shining in the darkness, where evil
    things abound.
Jesus is the lighthouse, showing us the
    way,
we can leave the darkness, live the
    Jesus way.

Jesus is the foghorn when trouble's very
    near,
when hidden dangers threaten, his
    warning sound you hear.
Jesus is the lighthouse, showing us the
    way,
we can miss the dangers, live the
    Jesus way.

Shine your light in me, Lord, I want to
    live for you,
help me shine for you, Lord, in all I say
    and do.
I want to be a lighthouse for Jesus
    ev'ry day,
help me make a difference in your world,
    I pray!

202 Paul Field

Jesus is the password, pass it on.
Jesus is the password, pass it on.
Don't keep it a secret, pass the news
    along.
Jesus is the password, pass it on.
Pass it on, pass it on, until everybody
    knows.
Pass it on, pass it on, that's the way the
    kingdom grows.
Pass it on, pass it on, until all the world
    has heard.
Pass it on, pass it on, that Jesus is Lord.

203 Roger Jones

*Jesus, I will come with you, I will follow
    in your way.
I will trust you, I will bring you all I
    have today.
Jesus, you're the way, Jesus, you're
    the truth,
Jesus, you're the life, praise your
    name!*

Amazing grace, how sweet the sound,
that could save a wretch like me.
I once was lost but now I'm found,
was blind but now I see.

Gentle Jesus, meek and mild,
look upon a little child.
Pity my simplicity,
loving him who first loved me.

Let us with a gladsome mind,
praise the Lord for he is kind.
For his mercies aye endure,
ever faithful, ever sure.

Praise God from whom all blessings
    flow,
praise him all creatures here below.
Praise him above ye heav'nly host,
praise Father, Son and Holy Ghost.

204 Philip Hawthorne

Jesus, Jesus, here I am;
Jesus, Jesus, take my hand.
You give to ev'ryone a love that won't
    end.
Thank you, Jesus, you're my friend.

205 Leon and Sheryl Olguin

Jesus, Jesus, I love you, I love you.
Jesus, Jesus, I love you, I love you.

Jesus, Jesus, I adore you, I adore you.
Jesus, Jesus, I adore you, I adore you.

You are lovely;
my eyes long to see your face,
and see the scars you bore for me.

Jesus, Jesus, I love you, I love you.
Jesus, Jesus, I love you, I love you,
I love you, I love you, I love you, I love
    you.

206 Sue Howson

Jesus, life giver.
Jesus, my Saviour.
Jesus, Jesus, Jesus.

You shed your blood
on Calvary.
You gave your life for me.

I come to you
to bow my knee.
You are my Lord and King.

207 Graham Kendrick

Jesus' love has got under our skin,
Jesus' love has got under our skin.
Deeper than colour oh;
richer than culture oh;
stronger than emotion oh;
wider than the ocean oh.
Don't you want to celebrate
and congratulate somebody,
talk about a family!
It's under our skin, under our skin.

Leader	Ev'rybody say love:
All	love.
Leader	Ev'rybody say love:
All	love,
Leader	love,
All	love.

Isn't it good to be
living in harmony.
Jesus in you and me;
he's under our skin,
under our skin,
he's under our skin,
under our skin.

208 H. W. Rattle

Jesus' love is very wonderful,
Jesus' love is very wonderful,
Jesus' love is very wonderful,
oh, wonderful love!
So high you can't get over it,
so low you can't get under it,
so wide you can't get round it,
oh, wonderful love!

209 Graham Kendrick

Jesus put this song into our hearts,
Jesus put this song into our hearts,
it's a song of joy no one can take
    away,
Jesus put this song into our hearts.

Jesus taught us how to live in
    harmony,
Jesus taught us how to live in
    harmony,
different faces, different races, he made
    us one,
Jesus taught us how to live in
    harmony.

Jesus taught us how to be a family,
Jesus taught us how to be a family,
loving one another with the love that
    he gives,
Jesus taught us how to be a family.

Jesus turned our sorrow into dancing,
Jesus turned our sorrow into dancing,
changed our tears of sadness into rivers
    of joy,
Jesus turned our sorrow into a dance.

210 Chris Jackson

Jesus, reign in me,
Jesus, reign in me;
take your place within my heart
and, Jesus, reign in me.

Jesus, you're my King,
Jesus, you're my King;
take your place within my heart
and, Jesus, you're my King.

Jesus, live in me,
Jesus, live in me;
take your place within my heart
and, Jesus, live in me.

Jesus, forgive me,
Jesus, forgive me;
take your place within my heart
and, Jesus, forgive me.

Jesus, I love you,
Jesus, I love you;
take your place within my heart
and, Jesus, I love you.

© 1988 Powerpack/Learning Curve Music

211 Sue Howson

Jesus, rock of my salvation,
Jesus, lover of my soul;
you alone give life that lasts for ever,
you alone can make me whole.
Call me up; call me higher.
Turn me towards you once again.
As the fragrance of your holiness
lingers in my heart,
I put my trust in you, my Lord and friend.

On this rock I will build my life.
On this rock I've found a love that satisfies.
On this rock I will live and never die.
On this rock I will build my life.

© 1996 Daybreak Music Ltd

212 Roger Jones

Jesus rode a donkey into town.
Many folks turned out from miles
  around.
What a sight to see,
a man to set men free,
riding on a donkey into town.

Jesus, is it true, the things the people
  say of you?
Did you really make a blind man see?
And if all I've heard about you turns out
  to be true,
can you really do the same for me?

Tell me, do you think he'll take the
  Roman guards by storm?
Do you think he'll show the priests the
  door?
Wonder if he's pleased by all the
  shouting from the crowd,
even by the palms upon the floor.

Hosanna, hosanna,
blessed is the man,
that cometh in the name,
cometh in the name of the Lord!
(Repeat)

© 1975 Christian Music Ministries/Sovereign Music UK

213 Derek Llewellyn

Jesus, send me the helper,
send me the helper to help me.
Jesus, send me the Holy Spirit,
send the Holy Spirit to me.

He gives us love to keep on loving.
He makes us brave to do what is right.
He gives us faith to keep on going.
He gives us power to keep us shining so
  bright.

© Sea Dream Music

214 Mike Burn

Jesus, thank you for the cross,
holding nothing back,
you did all your Father asked.
I'll never know just how it felt
as you died, lifted high.
I know it hurt, I know the pain
was more than words could ever say.
You had a choice,
you chose to die,
your sacrifice has saved my life,
what can I say?
Oh, Jesus, you gave your life for me,
so precious the blood you shed.
You made a way to heaven
by dying in my place.
Jesus, thank you for the cross.

215 Capt. Alan Price, CA

Jesus, touch me now,
please, I ask you, now.
Do your healing work in me,
your Spirit working tenderly,
make me the best that I can be,
O, Jesus, touch me now,
O, Jesus, touch me now.

Jesus, use me now,
please, I ask you, now.
Do your healing work through me,
your power working lovingly,
a useful servant I would be,
O, Jesus, use me now,
O, Jesus, use me now.

216 Capt. Alan Price, CA

Jesus wants me,
*Jesus wants me,**
Jesus wants me to follow him.

Jesus called to fishermen, said,
'Come, follow me!
Speak and heal with my power
and my authority.'

Jesus still calls his people,
there's a job to be done;
no matter who you are
there's a role for ev'ryone.

There's a cost to following,
of that we may be sure;
but we'll get back ev'rything we give
and even more.

* Last time
Jesus help us to follow you!

217 John Gibson

Jesus, we celebrate your victory;
Jesus, we revel in your love.
Jesus, we rejoice you've set us free;
Jesus, your death has brought us life.

It was for freedom that Christ has set us
    free,
no longer to be subject to a yoke of
    slavery;
so we're rejoicing in God's victory,
our hearts responding to his love.

His Spirit in us releases us from fear,
the way to him is open, with boldness
    we draw near.
And in his presence our problems
    disappear;
our hearts responding to his love.

218 Capt. Alan Price, CA

Jesus, we thank you;
Lord, you are here.
Thank you for loving us,
as we draw near.

219 Capt. Alan Price, CA

Jesus, you are here.
(Jesus you are here.)
Jesus, we know you're near.
(Jesus we know you.)

As a sign of worship
we lift our hands in praise,
because you've shown your love to us
in many different ways,
and we worship you, our Lord.

In our songs of worship
we lift our voice to you,
accept the love and thanks we bring
for all the things you do,
and we worship you, our Lord.

I lift my head up to you
in expectancy,
ready to receive your love,
your gift of grace to me,
and I worship you, my Lord.

220 Pete Simpson

Jesus, you are my King,
blessed Redeemer,
blessed Redeemer,
Jesus, you are my King,
blessed Redeemer.

Jesus, you are my Lord,
beautiful Saviour,
beautiful Saviour,
Jesus, you are my Lord,
beautiful Saviour.

Jesus, you are my rock,
King of the nations,
King of the nations,
Jesus, you are my rock,
King of the nations.

221 Bev Gammon

Jesus, you gave ev'rything for me,
and I want to learn to give to you
through the way I use my time,
my money and my talents;
help me give them all to please you.

222 Paul Crouch and David Mudie

Jesus, you're the King.
Lord of ev'rything.
You are God's son,
you're number one,
and that is why we sing.
(Repeat)

Jesus, you came down from heav'n
to the earth to serve us.
You died but then you rose again.
Glory, halleluia!

Help me to be more like you;
ev'ry day I need you.
I want to praise your name right now.
Here we go again!

223 Capt. Alan Price, CA

Just as the Father sent you, Lord,
with pow'r and authority;
just as the Father sent you, Lord,
so you are sending me.
I'm willing to be used, Lord,
in any way you choose,
I'll try not to be too busy
when it's me you want to use.
Just as the Father sent you, Lord,
with pow'r and authority;
just as the Father sent you, Lord,
I want you to send me.

© 1992 Daybreak Music Ltd

224 Capt. Alan Price, CA

Keep me close to you
in ev'rything I do today,
Jesus, help me to be careful
in ev'ry way*. Mm.

If I watch things that are bad for me,
things of which you'd disapprove,
help me to turn my eyes away,
or even get up and move.

When others use bad or dirty words,
help me to know what to do.
Stop me if ever I'm tempted
to do the same thing too.

If ever I get in bad places
with those who would cause me to stray,
Lord, let your light shine out from me,
or help me to get right away.

* Last time
  In all that I see and I say,
  in all that I hear and do,
  keep me, Lord, close to you. Mm.

© 1994 Daybreak Music Ltd

225 Mark and Helen Johnson

Let me tell you about a baby,
and his family.
It is written down in the Bible
so you might believe.
Many men had told of his coming,
down through history.
Now the time had come
for fulfilment of their prophecy.

  And they called his name Jesus,
  Jesus the Saviour.
  And they called his name Jesus,
  Son of the most high God.
  (Repeat)

There was once a young girl called Mary,
only in her teens.
She was visited by an angel,
sent to Galilee.
And he told her she'd have a baby,
how she couldn't see.
Yet it was her will to obey him,
so it was agreed.

Well, in those days Caesar Augustus
issued a decree,
and so Mary went with her husband
where they had to be.
There was nowhere else but a stable,
where they both could sleep.
It was there that she had her baby,
born for you and me.

© Out of the Ark Music

226 Jim Aldwinckle and Ron Sivers

Let's celebrate and clap our hands,
let's sing for joy and dance around;
let's raise our hands and praise his name,
for Jesus is our King.
Alleluia.

© Wellingborough Christian Centre

227 Kath Fathers

Let's get fit,
let's get fit,
let's get fit,
let's get fit.

It's time for the body to grow now,
it's time for the fruit to show now,
it's time for the world to know now,
so let's get fit.
It's time for the Church to fight now,
it's time to release the light now,
let's train with all our might now,
and let's get fit.

For those who worship the Lord,
the Son of righteousness will rise
with healing in his wings.
For those who worship the Lord,
the Son of righteousness will rise
with healing in his wings.
And you will break out and jump like
    calves from the stall
(break out and jump like calves from the
    stall),
break out and skip like calves from the
    stall
(break out and skip).

Let's get fit . . .

It's time to increase the pace now,
it's time for us all to race now,
let's step into his grace now,
and let's get fit.
Let all creation sing now,
he's giving us a time of spring now,
it's time for us all to win now,
so let's get fit.

© Chasah Music/Daybreak Music Ltd

228 Yvonne Scott

Let's sing and make music to the Lord.
Let's sing and make music to the Lord.
Give thanks to God the Father,
give thanks to Jesus his Son.
Give thanks to God the Father,
give thanks to Jesus his Son.

Let's praise and make music to the
    Lord.
Let's praise and make music to the
    Lord.
Give thanks to God the Father,
give thanks to Jesus his Son.
Give thanks to God the Father,
give thanks to Jesus his Son.

© 1996 Daybreak Music Ltd

229 Chris Jackson

Let us run with determination,
the race that lies before us;
let us keep our eyes fixed on Jesus.
Let us run with determination,
the race that lies before us;
let us keep our eyes fixed on Jesus.

© 1997 Powerpack/Learning Curve Music

230 Capt. Alan Price, CA

Let us sing and praise God for all that
    he has done,
for loving us so much in sending his
    Son.
Let us sing and let him know, let our
    praises overflow,
let us sing, let us shout, hallelujah!

Let us sing and praise God, let him
    know just how we feel,
by our words and actions, show our love
    for him is real.
Let us laugh, take a chance, lift our feet
    and have a dance,
as we sing, as we shout, hallelujah!

Let us pray to the Lord that we'll never
    let him down,
never let temptation cause our
    friendship to break down.
Holy Spirit come right in and keep us
    close to him,
always sing, always shout, hallelujah!

231   Paul Field

Let your love shine through these eyes
    of mine,
let me be a light for you each day.
Let your love show to ev'ryone I know,
help me learn to follow in your way.

Hand in hand for ever,
never let me go,
sure enough together,
wherever I may go.
No matter where life leads,
give me faith to see your plan,
so ev'ry step I take,
I take with you hand in hand.

Jesus, you are my bright shining star,
your word and your Spirit lead me on.
The best I can do, is a life shared with
    you,
only in your love can I be strong.

232   Capt. Alan Price, CA

Life is like a big wide ocean
and we're sailing the ocean with Jesus
our friend.
The journey is long and the weather
uncertain,
but Jesus is with us from beginning
to end.

Jesus knows the best course to sail.
Let's ask him to guide us.
Jesus knows the best course to sail,
with the Holy Spirit compass inside us!
Wa! Wa! Wa! Wa!

233   Doug Horley

Lift his name high,
let the world know
that the God of creation is alive
    and well.
Lift his name high,
let the world know
that the way to salvation,
the hope for our nation,
is Jesus, and he is alive.

Jesus is the King of glory,
this is no fairy story,
let the world know Jesus is alive.
Mending lives, hurt and broken,
words of healing spoken,
let the world know Jesus is alive.

234   Rick Founds

Lord, I lift your name on high;
Lord, I love to sing your praises.
I'm so glad you're in my life;
I'm so glad you came to save us.
(Repeat)

Continued overleaf

You came from heaven to earth
to show the way,
from the earth to the cross,
my debt to pay;
from the cross to the grave,
from the grave to the sky,
Lord, I lift your name on high.

235 Iain Craig

Lord, I want to be in your family,
Lord, I want to know I belong.
Lord, I want to be in your family,
I know that faith in you will make me
   strong.

I don't want to be the one
who says you're not for me,
I don't want to be left outside,
so, o, o, o, o, o,
Lord, I want to be in your family
where I can feel so safe and warm.

Now I know there might be times that I
   will let you down,
the things I say might not bless your name.
But Lord, I know you'll never let me go,
yesterday, today, for ever, you're the same.

236 Chris Jackson

Lord, look into my heart,
tell me what you see within me.
Lord, let your fire burn,
burn away the sin within me.
'Cos I want to know,
I want to know,
I want to put things right.

For I want to be,
I want to be holy in your sight.
Lord, look into my heart,
tell me what you see within me.

237 Graham Kendrick

Lord, the light of your love is shining,
in the midst of the darkness, shining;
Jesus, Light of the World, shine upon us,
set us free by the truth you now
   bring us.
Shine on me, shine on me.

Shine, Jesus, shine,
fill this land with the Father's glory;
blaze, Spirit, blaze,
set our hearts on fire.
Flow, river, flow,
flood the nations with grace and
*   mercy;*
send forth your word, Lord,
and let there be light.

Lord, I come to your awesome presence,
from the shadows into your radiance;
by the blood I may enter your
   brightness,
search me, try me, consume all my
   darkness.
Shine on me, shine on me.

As we gaze on your kingly brightness,
so our faces display your likeness,
ever changing from glory to glory;
mirrored here may our lives tell your
   story.
Shine on me, shine on me.

238 Ken McGreavy and Wes Sutton

Lord, we cry out to you.
Lord, we cry out to you.
Have mercy,
have mercy on us.

Open our eyes to see.
open our eyes to see.
We want to see,
we want to see you.

Lord we will follow you.
Lord we will follow you.
We'll follow you,
we'll follow in the way of truth.

239 Mick Ray

Lord, we give you praise;
our prayer of thanks to you we bring.
We sing our songs to you,
for praise belongs to you.
Lord, we give you praise.

Your love goes on and on;
you never change, you never turn.
Our hands we raise to you,
and bring our praise to you;
Lord, we give you praise.

240 Judy Bailey

Lord, we lift you high
when we praise your name,
when we worship you
and our hands are raised,
that is how we lift you up.
Lord, we lift you high
when we tell the truth,
when we give our best
in ev'rything we do,
that is how we lift you up.

By our voices be lifted, lifted,
by our actions, Lord, be lifted high.
By our love, Lord, be lifted, lifted,
by our lives, O Lord, be lifted high.

Lord, we lift you high
when we're good and kind;
when we turn from wrong
and we do what's right,
that is how we lift you up.
Lord, we lift you high
when we shine like stars;
when we tell our friends
just how good you are,
that is how we lift you up.

You are God, Jesus the Lord of all,
we place you above all else.
So shine through me
and keep drawing the world to your
heart.

241 Ian Smale

Lord, we've come to worship you,
Lord, we've come to praise;
Lord, we've come to worship you
in oh so many ways.
Some of us shout and some of us
sing,
and some of us whisper the praise we
bring;
but, Lord, we all are gathering
to give you our praise.

242 Ian Smale

Lord, you gave me joy in my heart,
joy in my heart always,
and it's you I want to praise.

Lord, you gave me peace in my mind,
peace in my mind always;
peace in my mind, joy in my heart,
and it's you I want to praise.

Lord, you gave me a song in my mouth,
a song in my mouth always;
a song in my mouth, peace in my mind,
  joy in my heart,
and it's you I want to praise.

Lord, you gave me hands that will clap,
hands that will clap always;
hands that will clap, a song in my
  mouth,
peace in my mind, joy in my heart,
and it's you I want to praise.

Lord, you gave me feet that can dance,
feet that can dance always;
feet that can dance, hands that will
  clap,
a song in my mouth, peace in my mind,
joy in my heart,
and it's you I want to praise.

Lord, you gave me a love for others,
a love for others always;
a love for others, feet that can dance,
hands that will clap, a song in my
  mouth,
peace in my mind, joy in my heart,
and it's you I want to praise.

© 1987 Kingsway's Thankyou Music

243 Ian Smale

Lord, you put a tongue in my mouth
and I want to sing to you.
Lord, you put a tongue in my mouth
and I want to sing to you.
Lord, you put a tongue in my mouth
and I want to sing only to you.
Lord Jesus, free us in our praise;
Lord Jesus, free us in our praise.

Lord, you put some hands on my arms
which I want to raise to you . . .

Lord, you put some feet on my legs
and I want to dance to you . . .

© 1983 Kingsway's Thankyou Music

244 Capt. Alan Price, CA

*Lord, you've promised through your
  Son,
you'll forgive the wrongs we've done;
we confess them, ev'ry one,
please, dear Lord, forgive us.*

Things we've done and things we've said,
we regret the hurt they spread.
Lord, we're sorry.
Lord, we're sorry.

Sinful and unkind thoughts too,
all of these are known to you.
Lord, we're sorry.
Lord, we're sorry.

And the things we've left undone,
words and deeds we should have done.
Lord, we're sorry.
Lord, we're sorry.

Last refrain:
Lord, you've promised, through your
*   Son,*
you'll forgive the wrong we've done;
we receive your pardon,
Lord, as you forgive us.

245 Derek Rowlinson

Love, love your enemies,
do good to those who hate you;
love, love your enemies,
do good to those who hate you.
Forgive others and God will forgive
    you,
give to others and God will give back;
forgive others and God will forgive
    you,
give to others and God will give back
    to you.

246 Jack W. Hayford

Majesty, worship his majesty,
unto Jesus be glory, honour and praise.
Majesty, kingdom authority
flows from his throne unto his own,
his anthem raise.
So exalt, lift up on high the name of
    Jesus;
magnify, come glorify Christ Jesus the
    King.
Majesty, worship his majesty,
Jesus who died, now glorified,
King of all kings.

247 Jimmy and Carol Owens

Make a joyful noise unto the Lord, all
    the earth,
make a joyful noise unto the Lord.
Make a joyful noise unto the Lord, all
    the earth,
make a joyful noise unto the Lord.
Make a loud noise (NOISE) and rejoice,
    sing praises,
make a joyful noise unto the Lord.
Make a loud noise (NOISE) and rejoice,
    sing praises,
make a joyful noise unto the Lord.

Where it says (NOISE) make a quick
*   sound – clap, whistle, shout, etc.*

248 Sebastian Temple

Make me a channel of your peace.
Where there is hatred, let me bring your
    love.
Where there is injury, your pardon, Lord,
and where there's doubt, true faith in you.

*   O Master, grant that I may never seek*
*   so much to be consoled as to console,*
*   to be understood, as to understand,*
*   to be loved, as to love with all my soul.*

Make me a channel of your peace.
Where there's despair in life, let me
    bring hope.
Where there is darkness, only light,
and where there's sadness, ever joy.

Make me a channel of your peace.
It is in pardoning that we are pardoned,
in giving of ourselves that we receive,
and in dying that we're born to eternal
    life.

249 Graham Kendrick

Make way, make way, for Christ the King
in splendour arrives;
fling wide the gates and welcome him
into your lives.

Make way (make way),
make way (make way),
for the King of kings
(for the King of kings);
make way (make way),
make way (make way),
and let his kingdom in!

He comes the broken hearts to heal,
the pris'ners to free;
the deaf shall hear, the lame shall dance,
the blind shall see.

And those who mourn with heavy hearts,
who weep and sigh,
with laughter, joy and royal crown
he'll beautify.

We call you now to worship him
as Lord of all,
to have no gods before him,
their thrones must fall.

250 David Ruis

Mercy is falling, is falling, is falling,
mercy it falls like the sweet spring rain.
Mercy is falling, is falling all over me.
(Repeat)

Hey O, I receive your mercy.
Hey O, I receive your grace.
Hey O, I will dance for evermore.
(Repeat)

251 Mark and Helen Johnson

Midnight, there's the strangest feeling in
the air tonight;
there's something going on but I can't
make it out,
I wonder what it's all about?
Starlight, breaking through the darkness
in the dead of night,
illuminates the path that takes you out
of sight,
and all the way to Bethlehem.

Tonight's events were planned in
heaven,
the greatest story ever penned.
Heaven and earth have come
together,
and life has come to Bethlehem.

Angels – taking care of things that only
they can do,
are waiting in the wings to bring the
joyful news,
it's going to turn the world around.
Strangers – having made arrangements
for a night or two,
have found accommodation in the
crowded rooms.
The house is packed in Bethlehem.

Shepherds – minding their own business
looking after things,
are startled by an unexpected
happening,
as angel choirs appear to them.
Wise men – taking charts and
telescopes and compasses,
investigate the star that takes them
travelling,
until they come to Bethlehem.

252 Robyn Barnett

Mind the gap! (I tell you).
Mind the gap! (don't fall down).
Mind the gap! (I heard him say).
You need to get across (but how?).
You need to get across (just look!).
You need to get across over the
    bridge.

Long ago when the world began,
we and God were best of friends,
walked and talked together all day
    long,
he never wanted this to end.
Then we let go of his strong hand,
chose to turn and walk away,
made a gap so deep and wide –
was this how we'd have to stay?

Think of things that we all do and say,
when we're selfish and unkind.
Broken objects we can stick and
    mend,
but not our broken hearts and lives.
Don't give up or feel despair,
whether girl or boy, woman or man.
God's the best friend we could have;
here's the story of his rescue plan.

It was just two thousand years ago,
Jesus Christ was born on earth;
he was so amazing, time was changed,
it began again from Jesus' birth!
He said, 'Look! I am the bridge!'
and the price he paid for wood and
    nails
was his life, but the price was right,
for the Cross shows love that never
    fails.

253 Julia Plaut

Mister Cow, how do you say to the Lord,
    'I love you?'
Mister Cow, how do you say to the Lord,
    'I love you?'
'Well I stand around in the field all day,
and it gives me plenty of time to say:
    Moo! Moo! Moo!'

Mister Sheep, how do you say to the
    Lord, 'I love you?'
Mister Sheep, how do you say to the
    Lord, 'I love you?'
'Well I stand around in the field all day,
and it gives me plenty of time to say:
    Baa! Baa! Baa!'

Mister Horse, how do you say to the
    Lord, 'I love you?'
Mister Horse, how do you say to the
    Lord, 'I love you?'
'Well I stand around in the field all day,
and it gives me plenty of time to say:
    Neigh! Neigh! Neigh!'

Mister Chicken, how do you say to the
    Lord, 'I love you?'
Mister Chicken, how do you say to the
    Lord, 'I love you?'
'Well I peck around in the yard all day,
and it gives me plenty of time to say:
    Cluck! Cluck! Cluck!'

Mister Pig, how do you say to the Lord,
    'I love you?'
Mister Pig, how do you say to the Lord,
    'I love you?'
'Well I roll around in the mud all day,
and it gives me plenty of time to say:
    Oink! Oink! Oink!'

Continued overleaf

Mister Fish, how do you say to the Lord,
   'I love you?'
Mister Fish, how do you say to the Lord,
   'I love you?'
'Well I swim around in the pond all day,
and it gives me plenty of time to say:
   Pop! Pop! Pop!'

Mister Duck, how do you say to the
   Lord, 'I love you?'
Mister Duck, how do you say to the
   Lord, 'I love you?'
'Well I swim around in the pond all day,
and it gives me plenty of time to say:
   Quack! Quack! Quack!'

254   Jim Bailey

Moses went down to see Pharaoh,
he said, 'Let my people go'.
Moses went down to see Pharaoh,
all Pharaoh could say was 'no'.
Moses turned his staff to a snake, oh,
he turned the Nile into blood.
'Pharaoh be fair, oh let my people go.'
Pharaoh said 'no' when he shouldn't have.

Moses went down to see Pharaoh,
Pharaoh not in a good mood.
He told Moses to 'hop it', and that
'Moses, you're going to get sued'.
Moses gave him a flea in the ear,
bugged him, got under his skin.
Pharaoh he cried, 'Pass the insecticide'.
Moses laughed, there were no flies on him.

   Pharaoh, let God's people go,
   will you ever know,
   God his pow'r will show?
   Pharaoh will you ever learn?
   Have you never heard,
   God has the last word?

Moses went down to see Pharaoh,
Pharaoh was not very pleased.
Pharaoh he came to boiling point,
when Egypt got mad cow disease.
But God, through Moses, wasn't finished
and, afflicted with terrible sores,
Pharaoh was to see God was bigger
   than he,
and that it never rains, it just pours.

Moses went down to see Pharaoh,
'Hail, Pharaoh,' he said, tongue in cheek.
'The locusts are coming to finish the job
and devour all there is left to eat.
Then darkness will cover the land oh,
just because you couldn't see.
Your firstborn will die, due to your
   stubborn pride,
and my people they will be set free.

255   Traditional

   My God is so big, so strong and
   *   so mighty,*
   there's nothing that he cannot do.
   My God is so big, so strong and
   *   so mighty,*
   there's nothing that he cannot do.

The rivers are his, the mountains are his,
the stars are his handiwork too.

He's called you to live for him ev'ry day,
in all that you say and you do.

256   Ian Smale

My God shall supply all my needs,
my God shall supply all my needs,
my God shall supply all my needs,
'cause it says so in the Bible.

'Cause it says so (where?)
in the book that came from heav'n,
'cause it says so (where?)
Isaiah fifty-eight elev'n.
My God shall supply all my needs,
'cause it says so in the Bible.

257   Darlene Zschech

My Jesus, my Saviour,
Lord, there is none like you.
All of my days
I want to praise
the wonders of your mighty love.
My comfort, my shelter,
tower of refuge and strength,
let ev'ry breath,
all that I am,
never cease to worship you.

Shout to the Lord, all the earth,
*   let us sing*
power and majesty, praise to the King.
Mountains bow down and the seas
*   will roar*
at the sound of your name.
I sing for joy
at the work of your hands.
For ever I'll love you, for ever I'll
*   stand.*
Nothing compares to the promise I
*   have in you.*

258   Noel and Tricia Richards

My lips shall praise you, my great
*   Redeemer;*
my heart will worship, Almighty
*   Saviour.*

You take all my guilt away,
turn the darkest night to brightest
    day;
you are the restorer of my soul.

Love that conquers ev'ry fear,
in the midst of trouble you draw near;
you are the restorer of my soul.

You're the source of happiness,
bringing peace when I am in distress;
you are the restorer of my soul.

259   Judy MacKenzie Dunn

My rock (my rock),
my rock (my rock),
you are (you are)
my strong foundation;
my rock (my rock),
my rock (my rock),
you are (you are)
my one salvation;
in you, oh Lord,
I will put my trust;
blessed be the Lord my rock.

260   Capt. Alan Price, CA

Na na na na na,
na na na na na na na na na.

There's a place waiting for me,
a place that's good to be,
I know, 'cos Jesus said it!
There's a place waiting for me,
a place that's good to be,
I know, 'cos Jesus said it!

Continued overleaf

He went to get it ready
for all who follow him;
I know, 'cos Jesus said it!
It's in his Father's house,
a house with many rooms;
it's true, 'cos Jesus said it!
If he went to get it ready,
he surely will return,
it's true, 'cos Jesus said it!
And when the time is right,
he'll take us there with him,
it's true, 'cos Jesus said it!

261   Capt. Alan Price, CA

Nobody liked Zacchaeus,
the small man from Jericho;
ev'ryone thought he was rotten,
Zacchaeus, he hated it so.

Now Zack, he heard about Jesus,
he climbed up a tree for a view;
said Jesus, 'I'm coming to your house
    today;
Zacchaeus, I'm talking to you!'

Oh, you'd better get off your back, Zack,
you'd better come down from the tree;
no matter what others may think of you,
to Jesus you're special, you see!

Because of the visit of Jesus,
Zacchaeus became someone new;
he gave four times as much as he'd
    cheated,
and half of his wealth away, too!

You might not be quite like Zacchaeus,
but sometimes you may feel quite blue.
The Bible is clear about one thing;
Jesus loves people like you!

Final chorus:
Oh, you'd better get off your back,
Whack,
you'd better just listen to me;
no matter what others may think of you,
to Jesus you're special, you see!

262   Capt. Alan Price, CA

Now I belong to Jesus and his Spirit
    lives in me,
I'm a soldier and a servant for the King
    of kings.
I'll fight against the wrong I find,
I'll serve him with my heart and mind,
a soldier and a servant I will be.
Make me faithful, Lord Jesus,
make me faithful, Lord, to you.
Keep me faithful, Lord Jesus,
keep me faithful, Lord, to you.

263   Sammy Horner

Obey the maker's instructions all the
    time.
Obey the maker's instructions and you
    will find;
obey the maker's instructions will help
    you see,
that things fit together much more easily.

So you can buy a model
of your favourite classic car,
without reading instructions
you put it together so far;
but when you think you're finished
you find a little extra bit,
it's the driver of the car
but now he just won't fit.

Say that you read the Bible
to see what God has said,
and you find instructions
and store them in your head;
but when you find that you're
    tempted
to doing things the wrong way,
instructions mean nothing
unless you do what they say.

He loves me so much,
he came to earth for me.
He loves me so much,
that he died for me.
But he came back to life again in victory,
all because he loves me.
Oh, it's so good to know,
oh, it's so good to know,
oh, it's so good to know
Jesus loves me.

264 Mike Burn

Oh, I'm fighting, but not against
    people,
it's a battle of good and evil;
but I don't need a gun, I don't need a
    sword,
I don't need sticks and I don't need
    stones.
My weapons are not of this world.
I'll fight with a prayer of faith,
I'll fight with a shout of praise;
my weapon is the Word of God.
It's sharper than any sword,
it cuts through the darkness of this
    world,
and the enemy's walls come crashing
    down,
as God's kingdom gets built.

265 Steve Burnhope

Oh, it's so good to know,
oh, it's so good.
Oh, it's so good to know
Jesus loves me.
(Repeat)

266 Unknown

Oh! Oh! Oh! how good is the Lord,
Oh! Oh! Oh! how good is the Lord,
Oh! Oh! Oh! how good is the Lord,
I never will forget what he has done
    for me.

He gives me salvation,
    how good is the Lord,
he gives me salvation,
    how good is the Lord,
he gives me salvation,
    how good is the Lord,
I never will forget
    what he has done for me.

He gives me his blessings . . .

He gives me his Spirit . . .

He gives me his healing . . .

He gives me his glory . . .

Other verses may be added as
    appropriate

267 Roger Jones

Oh, once there was a father,
who had two sons at home.
The young one wanted money,
so he could start to roam.

Lost! Lost! Lost and found!
That's what the Bible said!
Lost! Lost! Lost and found!
The son back from the dead.

He left home one bright morning,
he said, 'I must be free!
I'll go to the far country,
there's marv'lous sights to see!

He started spending money
on women, wine and song;
but this great time of plenty,
it didn't last too long!

He soon found he was starving,
the pigs he had to feed;
when he was back with father,
he never had a need!

He started back to father,
ashamed and all alone;
but father saw him coming,
and welcomed him back home!

268 Graham Kendrick

Leader Oh, the Lord is good;
All   oh, the Lord is good!
Leader The Lord is good;
All   the Lord is good!

Leader We want to hear you testify:
All   oh, the Lord is good.
Leader We want to hear you say:
All   the Lord is good.
Leader We want to hear it loud and strong:
All   oh, the Lord is good.
Leader We want to hear you shout:
All   the Lord is good!

Leader We want to hear the children say:
All   oh, the Lord is good.
Leader We want to hear you say:
All   the Lord is good.
Leader We want to hear you loud and strong:
All   oh, the Lord is good.
Leader We want to hear you shout:
All   the Lord is good!

Leader We want to hear the brothers say:
All   oh, the Lord is good.
Leader We want to hear you say:
All   the Lord is good.
Leader We want to hear the sisters say:
All   oh, the Lord is good.
Leader We want to hear you say:
All   the Lord is good.

Leader The younger to the older say:
Younger oh, the Lord is good.
Leader We want to hear you say:
Younger the Lord is good.
Leader Older to the younger say:
Older   oh, the Lord is good.
Leader We want to hear you say:
Older   the Lord is good.

Leader Let every generation say:
All   oh, the Lord is good.

Leader	We want to hear you say:
All	the Lord is good,
Leader	so good,
All	so good;
Leader	so kind,
All	so kind;
Leader	give him glory,
All	give him glory,
Leader	all the time,
All	all the time.

269 Doug Horley

Oi, oi, we are gonna praise the Lord.
Oi, oi, we are gonna praise the Lord.
Oi, oi, we are gonna praise the Lord.
He's an exciting, powerising, c-colossal,
humungousmungous

(Repeat)

God!

But it's sometimes hard to understand
that the God who made the earth and man
would point a finger down from heaven
      and shout:
'Hey you! I love you. Hey you! I love you.
Hey you, you! I love you.' – but it's true!'

270 Ian Smale

O Lord, you're great, you are fabulous,
we love you more than any words can
      sing, sing, sing.
O Lord, you're great, you are so generous,
you lavish us with gifts when we don't
      deserve a thing.

Allelu, alleluia, praise you, Lord.
Alleluia, praise you, Lord.
Alleluia, praise you, Lord.
(Repeat)

Oh Lord, you're great, you are so
      powerful,
you hold the mighty universe in your
      hand, hand, hand.
Oh Lord, you're great, you are so
      beautiful,
you've poured out your love on this
      undeserving land.

271 A. W. Edsor

On Calvary's tree he died for me,
that I his love might know.
To set me free he died for me,
that's why I love him so.

272 Ian White

Once there was a house, a busy little
      house,
and this is all about the busy little house.

Jesus Christ had come, teaching
      ev'ryone,
so ev'ryone has run to the busy little
      house.

Ev'ryone was there, you couldn't find a
      chair,
in fact you had to fight for air in the
      busy little house.

A man who couldn't walk was carried to
      the spot,
but the place was chock-a-block in the
      busy little house.

Whatever shall we do, whatever shall we
      do?
We'll never get him through into the
      busy little house.

Continued overleaf

We'll open up the roof, we'll open up the
   roof,
and then we'll put him through into the
   busy little house.

Then Jesus turned his eyes, and saw to
   his surprise
the man coming from the skies into the
   busy little house.

Then Jesus turned and said, 'Get up and
   take your bed,
and run along instead from the busy
   little house.'

273 Sydney Carter

One more step along the world I go,
one more step along the world I go.
From the old things to the new,
keep me travelling along with you.

   And it's from the old I travel to the
      new,
   keep me travelling along with you.

Round the corners of the world I turn,
more and more about the world I learn.
All the new things that I see
you'll be looking at along with me.

As I travel through the bad and good,
keep me travelling the way I should.
Where I see no way to go,
you'll be telling me the way, I know.

Give me courage when the world is
   rough,
keep me loving though the world is
   tough.
Leap and sing in all I do,
keep me travelling along with you.

You are older than the world can be,
you are younger than the life in me.
Ever old and ever new,
keep me travelling along with you.

274 Lisa Mazak

   One, two, three, Jesus loves me.
   One, two, Jesus loves you.

Three, four, he loves you more
than you've ever been loved before.

Five, six, seven, we're going to heav'n.
Eight, nine, it's truly divine.

Nine, ten, it's time to end;*
but instead we'll sing it again

Last time
There's no time to sing it again.

275 Judy MacKenzie Dunn

Only one of me,
only one of you,
only one of ev'ryone,
incredible but true.
Millions of us all,
none of us the same,
but God knows ev'ry single face
and ev'ry single name.

   Because he's so great, only God can
      do it,
   so great, that's why we sing.
   So great, I wish ev'rybody knew it,
   so great, that's why we worship him.

Ev'ry thought I think,
ev'ry prayer I pray,
ev'ry cry I cry to him and ev'rything
    I say,
in a world that's full of words
that swirl in space and time,
God's tuned in to all of them,
he knows which ones are mine.

276 Yvonne Scott

On my bed I remember you,
I remember you, O God.
On my bed I remember you,
you are my help.

*And I will praise you as long as I live,
and I will lift up my hands.
And I will praise you as long as I live,
and I will lift up my hands.*

When I wake I remember you,
I remember you, O God.
When I wake I remember you,
you are my help.

When I eat I remember you,
I remember you, O God.
When I eat I remember you,
you are my help.

When I play I remember you,
I remember you, O God.
When I play I remember you,
you are my help.

277 Ian Smale

On my tiptoes I am tall,
when I crouch down I am so small,
I stretch my hands out then I'm wide,
Jesus made me special.

Jesus loves me when I'm tall,
Jesus loves me when I'm small,
Jesus loves me when I'm wide,
Jesus made me special.

S - P - E - C - I - A - L,
S - P - E - C - I - A - L,
S - P - E - C - I - A - L,
Jesus made me special.

278 Robert Cull

Open our eyes, Lord,
we want to see Jesus,
to reach out and touch him
and say that we love him;
Open our ears, Lord,
and help us to listen;
O open our eyes, Lord,
we want to see Jesus!

279 Martin Smith

Over the mountains and the sea
your river runs with love for me,
and I will open up my heart
and let the Healer set me free.
I'm happy to be in the truth,
and I will daily lift my hands,
for I will always sing of
when your love came down.

*I could sing of your love for ever,
I could sing of your love for ever,
I could sing of your love for ever,
I could sing of your love for ever.*

O, I feel like dancing,
it's foolishness, I know;
but when the world has seen the light,
they will dance with joy
like we're dancing now.

280 Capt. Alan Price, CA

People brought children to Jesus,
to Jesus, to Jesus;
people brought children to Jesus,
to be touched by him.

But the disciples tried to stop them,
to stop them, to stop them;
but the disciples tried to stop them,
but they got it wrong!

Jesus was angry and he shouted,
he shouted, he shouted!
Jesus was angry and he shouted,
'Let them come to me!'

Jesus took the children in his arms,
in his arms, in his arms;
Jesus took the children in his arms,
gave them each a hug!

Jesus, please, I ask you, will you hug me
    too!
hug me too! hug me too!
Jesus, please, I ask you, will you hug me
    too,
for I am your child!

Hallelujah, hallelujah, hallelu!
Hallelu, hallelu!
Hallelujah, hallelujah, hallelu!
Jesus loves me!

281 Unknown

Peter and John went to pray,
they met a lame man on the way.
He asked for alms and held out his palms,
and this is what Peter did say:

'Silver and gold have I none,
but such as I have I give you;
in the name of Jesus Christ of Nazareth,
rise up and walk!'

He went walking and leaping and
    praising God,
walking and leaping and praising God.
'In the name of Jesus Christ of Nazareth,
rise up and walk.'

282 Capt. Alan Price, CA

Please fill me, Lord, with your power,
pow'r to live for you;
Holy Spirit, ev'ry hour,
let your love flow through.

When you died on Calvary,
I know it was in love for me.
Lord, I know your loving care
is for people ev'rywhere.

Lord, I want to live for you,
live the way you want me to,
do the things that make you glad,
not the things that make you sad.

283 Andy Piercy and Dave Clifton

Praise God from whom all blessings flow,
praise him, all creatures here below.
Praise him above, you heav'nly host,
praise Father, Son and Holy Ghost.
(Repeat)

Give glory to the Father,
give glory to the Son,
give glory to the Spirit
while endless ages run.
'Worthy the Lamb,' all heaven cries,
'to be exalted thus.'
'Worthy the Lamb,' our hearts reply,
'for he was slain for us.'

Praise God from whom all blessings flow.
Praise God from whom all blessings flow.
Praise God from whom all blessings flow.
Praise God from whom all blessings flow.

284 John Kennett

Praise him on the trumpet,
the psaltery and harp,
praise him on the timbrel
   and the dance;
praise him with stringed instruments too.
Praise him on the loud cymbals,
praise him on the loud cymbals,
let ev'rything that has breath
praise the Lord.

Hallelujah, praise the Lord,
hallelujah, praise the Lord,
let ev'rything that has breath
praise the Lord.
(Repeat)

285 Mike Burn

Pray at all times, never ceasing,
ask for what you need with
   thanksgiving.
Join together in agreement
and together we'll see the kingdom
   come.

Give thanks to the Father,
for he hears all our prayers.
Give thanks to the Son,
for he prays for us.
Give thanks to the Spirit,
for when we don't know how to pray
he will plead with God on our behalf.

286 Paul Crouch and David Mudie

Prayer is like a telephone
for us to talk to Jesus.
Prayer is like a telephone
for us to talk to God.
Prayer is like a telephone
for us to talk to Jesus.
Pick it up and use it ev'ry day.
We can shout out loud,
we can whisper softly,
we can make no noise at all,
but he'll always hear our call.

287 Roger Jones

Riding high and low,
looking for a king,
riding over deserts,
with the gifts we bring.

Frankincense and myrrh,
gold we bring to him,
these are what we'll give,
and our hearts to him.

Over mountains high,
over deserts dry,
on to find this baby,
looking in the sky!

Continued overleaf

Frankincense and myrrh,
gold we bring to him,
these are what we'll give,
and our hearts to him.

On we go to Herod,
but he'll turn so green,
when we tell of Jesus,
and the star we've seen.

We are nearly there,
might get there today;
star is still above us,
showing us the way.

288   Unknown

Rise, and shine, and give God the
* glory, glory.*
Rise, and shine, and give God the
* glory, glory.*
Rise, and shine, and give God the
* glory, glory,*
children of the Lord.

The Lord said to Noah: 'There's gonna
  be a floody, floody.'
Lord said to Noah: 'There's gonna be a
  floody, floody.
Get those children out of the muddy,
  muddy,
children of the Lord.'

The Lord told Noah to build him an arky,
  arky,
Lord told Noah to build him an arky,
  arky.
Build it out of gopher barky, barky,
children of the Lord.

The animals, the animals, they came on,
  by twosies, twosies,
animals, the animals, they came on, by
  twosies, twosies.
Elephants and kangaroosies, 'roosies,
children of the Lord.

It rained and poured for forty daysies,
  daysies,
rained and poured for forty daysies,
  daysies.
Almost drove those animals crazies,
  crazies,
children of the Lord.

The sun came out and dried up the
  landy, landy,
sun came out and dried up the landy,
  landy.
Ev'rything was fine and dandy, dandy,
children of the Lord.

289   Mark and Helen Johnson

Risen! Risen! Jesus is risen!
The Spirit was given, Jesus is alive!*

Early in the morning, on the first day of
  the week,
women went to visit at the tomb;
angels came and told them: 'The one
  you've come to see,
he isn't here, but you will meet him
  soon!'

Fearful and excited, amazed by all they'd
  seen,
Mary and her friends ran from the tomb:
finding the disciples together where
  they'd meet,
bursting with joy, they ran into the
  room!

Two of the believers, with thoughts
  about the week,
walked the road so lonely and
  confused.
While they spoke of Jesus, and all he'd
  come to mean,
he came along beside them with the
  news.

All of his disciples were terrified to see
Jesus before them in the room.
'Why are you so frightened?' he said,
  'It's really me!
All of the things I told you have come
  true!'

*Last time
Risen! Risen! Jesus is risen!

© Out of the Ark Music

290 Paul Field

Safe in the Father's hands,
we are safe in the Father's hands.
There may be things we don't
  understand,
we're safe in the Father's hands.

So many things we'll never learn,
no matter how hard we try.
Though we may feel small,
the maker of all watches with loving
  eyes.

Trusting in God, we can be sure
no matter where life may lead,
his promises told, he's in control,
he's ev'rything we need.

© 1995 Windswept Pacific Music/Music Sales Ltd

291 Michael Perry

See him lying on a bed of straw,
a draughty stable with an open door.
Mary cradling the babe she bore:
the Prince of Glory is his name.

  Oh, now carry me to Bethlehem,
  to see the Lord of love again:
  just as poor as was the stable then,
  the Prince of Glory when he came!

Star of silver, sweep across the skies,
show where Jesus in a manger lies;
shepherds, swiftly from your stupor rise
to see the Saviour of the world!

Angels, sing again the song you sang,
sing the story of God's gracious plan;
sing that Bethl'em's little baby can
be the Saviour of us all.

Mine are riches from your poverty;
from your innocence, eternity;
mine, forgiveness by your death for me,
child of sorrow for my joy.

© Mrs B. Perry/Jubilate Hymns

292 Karen Lafferty

Seek ye first the kingdom of God
and his righteousness,
and all these things shall be added unto
  you,
hallelu, hallelujah!

  Hallelujah! Hallelujah!
  Hallelujah! Hallelu, hallelujah!

You shall not live by bread alone,
but by every word
that proceeds from the mouth of God,
hallelu, hallelujah!

Continued overleaf

Hallelujah! Hallelujah!
Hallelujah! Hallelu, hallelujah!

Ask and it shall be given unto you,
seek and you shall find.
Knock and it shall be opened unto you,
hallelu, hallelujah.

If the Son shall set you free,
you shall be free indeed.
You shall know the truth and the truth
    shall set you free,
hallelu, hallelujah!

Let your light so shine before men
that they may see your good works
and glorify your Father in heaven,
hallelu, hallelujah!

Trust in the Lord with all your heart,
he shall direct your paths,
in all your ways acknowledge him,
hallelu, hallelujah!

© 1972 Maranatha! Music/CopyCare

293 David Graham

Shake a friend's hand,
shake a hand next to ya,
shake a friend's hand and sing la la;
shake a friend's hand,
shake a hand next to ya,
shake a friend's hand and sing,
sing a la la la la la laleluia,
la la la la laleluia.
La la la la la laleluia,
la la la la laleluia!

Hug a friend's neck,
hug a neck next to ya . . .

Squeeze a friend's knee,
squeeze a knee next to ya . . .

Scratch a friend's back,
scratch a back next to ya . . .

Jesus is a friend,
he's a friend next to ya . . .

Don't just stand in your own little place,
reach out and touch a friend.
Give of yourself and you will find
the blessings never end!

© CA Music/Music Services/Copycare

294 Andrew and Pauline Pearson

Shake those hands,
wiggle those feet,
nod that head,
in case it's still asleep.
(Repeat)

> *Wake up and praise the Lord,*
> *wake up and praise the Lord,*
> *wake up and praise the Lord*
> *with all of me.*

© 1997 Daybreak Music Ltd

295 Paul Crouch and David Mudie

Shoop shoop doobee doo doo,
there's nobody who loves me like
    you do.
Shoop shoop doobee doo doo,
nobody's a friend like you.

Wop bop doobee doo waa,
we sing your name and shout
    hallelujah.
Wop bop doobee doo waa,
King of kings for ever you are!

Shoop shoop doobee doo doo,
I shout your name and sing hallelujah.
Shoop shoop doobee doo doo,
only you can make my life new.

Wop bop doobee doo waa,
we sing your name and shout
    hallelujah.
Wop bop doobee doo waa,
King of kings for ever you are.

Shoop shoop doobee doo doo,
you're ev'rything that ever was true now.
Shoop shoop doobee doo doo,
I want to tell my friends about you.

Wop bop doobee doo waa,
we sing your name and shout
    hallelujah.
Wop bop doobee doo waa,
King of kings for ever you are!

© 1995 Daybreak Music Ltd

296 Chris Jackson

*Sing and shout your praise to our
    God,
he alone is King.
He's the ruler of the earth,
he's the Lord of ev'rything.*

He is a mighty God,
full of majesty,
glory and honour and pow'r.
So come and praise him,
shout aloud,
lift his name on high.

The Lord is merciful,
loving and kind;
faithful and gentle is he.
So come and worship him,
bow the knee,
magnify his name with me.

© 1998 Powerpack/Learning Curve Music

297 Mark and Helen Johnson

Sing a song, sing a joyful song,
sing a joyful song to celebrate!
Sing a song, sing a joyful song,
sing a joyful song to celebrate!

*Jesus is alive, you know,
he's risen from the dead!
He was crucified
but now he's risen like he said.
(Hallelujah!)*

Clap your hands, clap your hands like this,
clap your hands like this to celebrate!
Clap your hands, clap your hands like this,
clap your hands like this to celebrate!

Jump up and down, up and down and
    around,
up and down and around to celebrate!
Jump up and down, up and down and
    around,
up and down and around to celebrate!

Dance to the beat, to the beat of the
    drum,
to the beat of the drum to celebrate!
Dance to the beat, to the beat of the
    drum,
to the beat of the drum to celebrate!

Wave your hands, wave your hands in
    the air,
wave your hands in the air to celebrate!
Wave your hands, wave your hands in
    the air,
wave your hands in the air to celebrate!

Sing a song, sing a joyful song,
sing a joyful song to celebrate!
Sing a song, sing a joyful song,
sing a joyful song to celebrate!

© Out of the Ark Music

298 Derek Llewellyn

Sing praise to God the Father,
God the Spirit, God the Son.
Sing praise to God who loves us,
praise him ev'ryone.

Sing praise to God the Father,
clap your hands and jump for joy.
He made the world around us,
and he loves us all.

Sing praise to God's Son Jesus,
clap your hands and jump for joy.
Wave your arms and turn around.
He teaches us about the Father,
and he loves us all.

Sing praise to the Holy Spirit,
clap your hands and jump for joy.
Wave your arms and jump around,
stamp your feet and shout hooray.
He helps us to live like Jesus
and he loves us all.

299 Ian Smale

So if you think you're standing firm,
be careful you don't fall;
so if you think you're standing firm,
be careful you don't fall;
so if you think you're standing firm,
be careful you don't fall;
so if you think you're standing firm,
be careful you don't fall.

300 Nick Harding

So I'll trust (so I'll trust)
in God (in God),
wherever I am,
I know I can,
so I'll trust (so I'll trust),
in God (in God),
'cos God has got a plan,
God has got a plan.

God was, God is and always will be.
He knows what I hear and do and see.
He made me, loves me, leads me too.
He's got a plan for me and you.

God was, and God is with me here,
he sent his Son, he takes my fear,
his Spirit lives deep in my heart –
I'm in his plan right from the start.

301 Ian Smale

So I've made up my mind,
that I'm gonna follow him,
wherever Jesus leads me I will go.
(Repeat)

I may be scared
by the things I see,
but Jesus won't
let them destroy me.

I may be scared
by the things I hear,
but Jesus won't
let me live in fear.

I may be scared
by the things I know,
but Jesus won't
ever let me go.

302 Capt. Alan Price, CA

Some people are fat, some people are
   thin,
but we've all got a problem with a thing
   called sin;
some people are pink, some people are
   brown,
but no matter what the colour, we're the
   same deep down!

No matter who we are,
God loves us ev'ry one;
to make us his friends again,
he gave his only Son.

Some people we like, some people we
   don't,
but how can we love our neighbour if
   try we won't?
God's help is at hand, we just need to
   ask,
and God the Holy Spirit will help us in
   the task.

303 Sammy Horner

Some people laugh, some people sing,
some people clap, and so they bring
their worship to the King of kings.
What do you do? What do you do?

Some people dance, some bring a word,
some people cry before the Lord,
and so they bring their worship to
the King of kings, the King of kings.

Some people march and raise their hands,
and some are quiet, but understand
there are many ways of worshipping
the King of kings, the King of kings.

304 Paul Field

Some things make you angry and some
   things can make you shout;
sometimes you can't keep it in, you've
   got to let it out;
but before you lose your temper, stop!
Count to ten and say a prayer for love.

Count to ten and say a prayer,
Jesus always will be there,
count to ten and talk to him,
let him put his love within* your heart.
One, two, three, four, five,
six, seven, eight, nine, ten.

Angry words can hurt someone much
   more than sticks or stones,
so when you feel your temper rising to
   the danger zone,
close your eyes and keep your lips shut
   tight,
count to ten and say a prayer for love.

* Last time
   Say a prayer for love.

305 Chris Mercer

Sometimes in the morning
I feel sad, sad, sad,
so I just ask Jesus,
make my sad heart glad.

Wake up and dance for joy,
wake up and dance for joy,
wake up and dance for joy,
first thing in the morning.

Sometimes in the morning,
I feel glad, glad, glad,
so I just praise Jesus,
for the day I'll have.

306 Ian Smale

So we're marching along, singing a
    song,
we're in the Lord's army.
We're fighting for right as we're learning
    what's wrong,
'cause we're in the Lord's army.
He's got the victory, so let's really shout,
we're in the Lord's army.
We're in the Lord's (yeah),
we're in the Lord's (right),
we're in the Lord's army.

307 Chris Jackson

Speak, Lord, I am your servant,
I am list'ning to your voice.
Speak, Lord, I am your servant,
I am list'ning.

308 Capt. Alan Price, CA

Special agents, we're special agents,
for J - E - S - U - S.
He called us and we said 'yes',
we'll be his special agents,
special agents.

We're special 'cos we know his care,
a love that's so tremendous.
We're agents for Jesus the King,
'cos he's the one who sends us!

We'll use our eyes to see just where
God is working around us.
We'll use our ears to listen, too,
and act on what he tells us!

309 Judy Bailey

Spirit (Spirit),
Holy Spirit (Holy Spirit),
fall on me.
Spirit (Spirit),
Holy Spirit (Holy Spirit),
fall on me.

I want to know that your presence is near,
I want to know that your power is here.
I want the weight of your glory to fall on
    me,
so come now Holy . . .

Spirit (Spirit) . . .

We welcome you here,
we welcome you here,
we welcome you here,
we need you, we need you.

I want to know that you're here in this
    place,
healing our lives and enlarging our faith.
I want to know when I leave there's a
    change in me,
so come now Holy . . .

Spirit (Spirit) . . .

We welcome you . . .

310 Mark and Helen Johnson

Sun and the moon and the starlit sky,
God created them all.
Rivers and seas and the oceans wide,
he created them all.
Forests and fields and the deserts dry,
God created them all.
Valleys and foothills and mountains high,
he created them all.

God looked down from heaven,
he was pleased, oh yeah!
Ev'rything was just as it should be,
ah ha!*

Every creature that moves and breathes,
God created them all.
Fliers and swimmers and some with feet,
he created them all.
Beautiful flowers and fruitful trees,
God created them all.
Every plant that you'll ever see,
he created them all.

Summer and autumn and winter, spring,
God created them all.
Each of the changes the seasons bring,
he created them all.
Thunder and lightning, the rain and wind,
God created them all.
Glorious sunsets and snowy scenes,
he created them all.

* Last time
God created the whole wide world, he
    created it all!

© Out of the Ark Music

311 Ian White

S - U - N is shining in the sky,
S - U - N is shining in the sky,
bringing light, bringing light all around.
(Repeat)

But S - O - N, the Son who came to die,
S - O - N, the Son who came to die,
bringing life, bringing life all around.

And if you have the Son you have life,
oh, if you have the Son you have life,
oh, if you have the Son you have life,
you have life in abundance.

© 1987 Little Misty Music/Kingsway's Thankyou Music

312 Graham Kendrick and
Steve Thompson

Teach me to dance
to the beat of your heart,
teach me to move
in the pow'r of your Spirit,
teach me to walk
in the light of your presence,
teach me to dance
to the beat of your heart.
Teach me to love
with your heart of compassion,
teach me to trust
in the word of your promise,
teach me to hope
in the day of your coming,
teach me to dance
to the beat of your heart.

You wrote the rhythm of life,
created heaven and earth,
in you is joy without measure.
So, like a child in your sight,
I dance to see your delight,
for I was made for your pleasure,
pleasure.

Let all my movements express
a heart that loves to say 'yes',
a will that leaps to obey you.
Let all my energy blaze
to see the joy in your face;
let my whole being praise you,
praise you.

© 1993 Make Way Music

313 Unknown

Thank you, Jesus, thank you, Jesus,
thank you, Lord, for loving me.
Thank you, Jesus, thank you, Jesus,
thank you, Lord, for loving me.

Continued overleaf

You went to Calvary,
and there you died for me.
Thank you, Lord, for loving me.
(Repeat)

Thank you, Jesus, thank you, Jesus,
thank you, Lord, for loving me.
Thank you, Jesus, thank you, Jesus,
thank you, Lord, for loving me.

You rose up from the grave,
to me new life you gave,
thank you, Lord, for loving me.
(Repeat)

You're coming back again,
and we with you shall reign.
Thank you, Lord, for loving me.
(Repeat)

314 Capt. Alan Price, CA

Thank you very much!
Thank you very much!
Thank you very much for all you do
for me!
Thank you very much!
Thank you very much!
Thank you very much for all you mean
to me!

There's so many things I often take for
granted,
things I hardly think about,
I just know that they're there!
But I want to take the time to tell you
that I'm grateful.
Thank you for the many things that
prove you really care!

315 John MacPherson

The blessing of God be upon you
and around you, wherever you go.
The blessing of God be within you
and among you, wherever you go.
Wherever you go, whatever you do,
may the blessing of God go with you.

316 Doug Horley

The gift of God is eternal life through
Jesus Christ,
the gift of God is eternal life through
Jesus Christ,
the gift of God is eternal life through
Jesus Christ,
through Jesus, Jesus Christ.
Jesus is the boss of my life,
he's the only one can make it come right;
Jesus is the boss of my life, Jesus is the
boss.

Leader	I'm a friend of Jesus Christ,
All	I'm a friend of Jesus Christ.
Leader	He's God's Son and he's alive,
All	he's God's Son and he's alive.
Leader	I will trust in him, it's true,
All	I will trust in him, it's true.
Leader	He's always there to see me through,
All	he's always there to see me through.
Leader	Sound off –
All	Jesus,
Leader	Sound off –
All	is Lord.
Leader	Sound off –
All	Jesus,
Leader	Sound off –
All	is Lord!

Rap

I said, come on ev'rybody and move
    your feet,
the rhythm is hot, it's a powerful beat.
The time is right to do some business,
get on your feet and be a witness
to the Holy One,
the King of kings, God's only Son.
Jesus Christ, that's his name,
he died to take our sin and shame.

317 Capt. Alan Price, CA

The joy of the Lord is a great thing,
quite different from anything I know.
Jesus in my life makes my heart sing,
despite the things that make me feel
    quite low.
It's a joy from deep inside, only Jesus
    can provide,
I'm gonna let the joy of Jesus overflow!
It's a joy from deep inside, only Jesus
    can provide,
I'm gonna let the joy of Jesus overflow!

318 Richard Hubbard

The promise of the Holy Spirit
is for you.
The promise of the Holy Spirit
is for your children.
The promise of the Holy Spirit
is for all who are far off,
even as many as the Lord your God
    shall call.
Oh yeah!
Acts, chapter two, verse thirty-nine.

319 Paul Crouch and David Mudie

The race that we are running
may be hard, it may be tough,
But in his word God promised
that his strength would be enough
to see us to the finish line,
and there to claim the prize
that Jesus died to win for us –
resurrection life.

We're running, we're running,
we're focused on the goal.
We're pressing on,
we're getting there,
we will not trip and fall.
We're running, we're running,
we'll put our trust in him.
Even though it's tough we know
God will help us win.

320 John Gowans

There are hundreds of sparrows,
    thousands, millions,
they're two a penny, far too many there
    must be;
there are hundreds and thousands,
    millions of sparrows,
but God knows ev'ry one, and God
    knows me.

There are hundreds of flowers,
    thousands, millions,
and flowers fair the meadows wear for
    all to see;
there are hundreds and thousands,
    millions of flowers,
but God knows ev'ry one, and God
    knows me.

Continued overleaf

There are hundreds of planets,
    thousands, millions,
way out in space each has a place by
    God's decree;
there are hundreds and thousands,
    millions of planets,
but God knows ev'ry one, and God
    knows me.

There are hundreds of children,
    thousands, millions,
and yet their names are written on God's
    memory,
there are hundreds and thousands,
    millions of children,
but God knows ev'ry one, and God
    knows me.

321 Steve Burnhope

There are lots of ways that I can praise,
there are very many things that I can do;
there are lots of ways that I can praise,
and show you, Lord, how much I love
    you.
I can touch my toes, I can hold my nose,
I can crouch down low, I can jump up
    high.
I can clap like this, I can do the twist,
but the thing that I do best is shout, 'I
    love you, Lord!'

322 Capt. Alan Price, CA

There are so many stories that I love to
    hear,
I picture the scenes in my head.
In books or on TV they also appear,
I think of them all in my head.

But the stories of Jesus are different you
    see,
'cos he's a real person who loves you
    and me.
Though I can't see him, I know he is real;
Jesus is my best friend.

So tell me the stories of Jesus,
over and over and over again;
tell me the stories of Jesus,
over and over again.

There are so many stories that I love to
    hear,
I picture the scenes in my head.
In books or on TV they also appear,
I think of them all in my head.
But the story of Jesus is different I know,
'cos he's a real person who lived long
    ago.
Though he's in heaven, his Spirit is here,
that's how he's my best friend.

323 Doug Horley, Belinda Horley and
Penny Roberts

There is a God who knows your name,
there is a God who feels your pain;
there is a love holding out for you,
don't turn away, let him love you.

'Cos he loves you with a passion, an
    endless raging fire,
from eternity to eternity you are his
    heart's desire.
And if you could for a moment glimpse
    the hugeness of his heart,
you'd see how he simply loves you.

He loves you with a passion, he's always
   on your side,
like a mighty wave that won't be
   stopped, his love is ocean wide.
Higher than the heavens above, and
   deeper than the sea;
truth is, just this, he simply loves you.

When you feel you've fallen far too far to
   ever stand again,
and you can't believe this Holy God
   could ever be your friend,
he's shouting from the heavens above,
   he's there to help you through,
you'll see how he simply loves you;
truth is, just this, he simply loves you.

324 Kath Fathers

There is a place where I can go,
when I'm feeling lonely or afraid.
There is a place where I can go,
that is special to me.
There is a love that's kind and warm,
a love that will kiss and comfort me.
There is a place where I can go,
that is special to me.

   No one loves me like Jesus loves me,
   in his arms I'm happy.
   No one knows me like Jesus knows me,
   no one knows like he knows.
   No one loves like he loves,
   he loves me.

There is a secret place to go,
where somebody knows me very well.
There is a secret place to go,
where I can be me.
And there my loving Jesus smiles,
he opens his arms and welcomes me.
There is a secret place to go,
where I can be me.

Oh Jesus,
no one loves me the way you love me,
in your arms I'm happy.
No one knows me the way you know me,
no one knows like you know.
No one loves like you love,
you love me.

325 Paul Field

There is no one else like you,
there's no one else like me.
Each of us is special to God,
that's the way it's meant to be.
I'm special, you're special,
we're special, don't you see,
there is no one else like you,
there's no one else like me.
Black or white, short or tall,
good or bad, God loves us all.
Loud or quiet, fat or thin,
each of us is special to him.

326 Noel Richards

There is pow'r in the name of Jesus;
we believe in his name.
We have called on the name of Jesus;
we are saved! We are saved!
At his name the demons flee.
At his name captives are freed,
for there is no other name that is higher
than Jesus!

Continued overleaf

There is pow'r in the name of Jesus,
like a sword in our hands.
We declare in the name of Jesus
we shall stand! We shall stand!
At his name God's enemies
shall be crushed beneath our feet,
for there is no other name that is higher
than Jesus!

327 Capt. Alan Price, CA

There is so much to discover,
that God wants us to know.
There is so much to find out for
  ourselves,
and that's the way to go.
When we learn what God has said,
when we act on what we've read,
there is so much to discover,
there's so much more to know.

There is so much to discover,
that God wants us to know.
There is so much to find out for
  ourselves,
and that's the way to go.
Through the Spirit's pow'r within,
we can change the world for him.
There is so much to discover,
there's so much more to know.

There is so much to discover,
that God wants us to know.
There's so much to find out for
  ourselves,
and that's the way to go.
If we're ever feeling bored,
we just need to ask the Lord
to show to us the things he's planned
  for us to do,
and that's the way to go.

328 Capt. Alan Price, CA

There, on a cruel cross, for all to see;
killed like a criminal, how could it be?
That Jesus bore such pain and shame,
mock'd by those who only came
to stand and watch, yet still not see
what God was doing then, for you and me.

There, on a cruel cross, so painfully;
killed like a criminal, yet willingly.
Lord Jesus bore such pain and shame,
for that is why he really came;
the greatest act of history,
what God was doing then, for you and me.

Lord, I may never understand,
or know the reason why
the only way to be forgiv'n,
was that you should die;
I worship you; I follow you;
I live for you; I trust in you.

329 Unknown

There once was a man called Daniel
  (good old Daniel),
and Daniel prayed three times a day
  (good old Daniel);
but the king's decree said 'Worship me!'
  (poor old Daniel),
but Daniel would not bend the knee!
  (good old Daniel).
So the gates went 'crash' (crash),
and the locks went 'click' (click),
and the lions began to (roar),
and the lions began to (roar),
but they couldn't eat Daniel if they tried
  (good old Daniel),
because the Lord was on his side (good
  old Daniel).

330
Doug Horley and Vanessa Freeman

There's a King above the heavens,
there's a King above the earth,
and from out of timeless history,
he brought mankind to birth.
And when sin brought separation,
and tore the heart of the King,
he sent his son, Jesus Christ,
a sacrifice for sin.

Hoop sah oh, oh, oh.
Hoop sah oh, oh, oh.
Hoop sah oh.
Hoop sah oh.
(Repeat)

Let the rhythm move your spirit,
let the rhythm touch your soul.
It's the sound of love, the sound of life,
it's the sound of hope.
Let the truth be seen by people
as he is lifted high.
May nations turn, may nations find
the hope in Jesus Christ.

There's a cry rising up. (Lift him high.)
There's a cry rising up. (He's alive.)
There's a cry rising up. (Oh, oh, oh, it's
    Jesus.)
(Repeat)

King of heaven,
King of heaven,
King of heaven, we lift you high.
(Repeat)

331
Ian Smale

There's nothing better than being a
    soldier
in the army of the Lord.
There's nothing better than being a
    soldier
in the army of the Lord.
We'll live by faith and not by sight,
not by power, not by might,
but by his Spirit win ev'ry fight.

332
Ian Smale

There's nothing I like better than to praise.
There's nothing I like better than to praise.
'Cos, Lord, I love you,
and there's nothing I would rather do
than whisper about it, talk all about it,
shout all about it all my days.

333
Roger Jones

There were ninety-nine sheep back safe
    in the fold,
but one of them's left outside in the cold.
The shepherd was wond'ring,
'Oh where, tell me where can it be?
    Can it be?
Where? Where? Where's the missing
    one?
Where? Where? Where's the missing one?
Oh, where can it be?'

So the shepherd set out in dead of the
    night,
the wind and the rain, a pitiful sight.
He kept right on searching,
but no sheep at all could he see!
Could he see!
Where? Where? Where's the missing one?
Where? Where? Where's the missing one?
Oh, where can it be?

Continued overleaf

But the shepherd, at last, he found his
    lost sheep,
all ragged and cold and trying to sleep.
He picked it right up
and he carried it home. Now it's found!
Now it's found!
There! There! There's the missing one!
There! There! There's the missing one!
And now it is found!

334 Damian Lundy

The Spirit lives to set us free,
walk, walk in the light.
He binds us all in unity,
walk, walk in the light.

Walk in the light,
walk in the light,
walk in the light,
walk in the light of the Lord.

Jesus promised life to all,
walk, walk in the light.
The dead were wakened by his call,
walk, walk in the light.

He died in pain on Calvary,
walk, walk in the light,
to save the lost like you and me,
walk, walk in the light.

We know his death was not the end,
walk, walk in the light.
He gave his Spirit to be our friend,
walk, walk in the light.

The Spirit lives in you and me,
walk, walk in the light.
His light will shine for all to see,
walk, walk in the light.

335 Mick Gisbey

The time has come to have some fun,
don't stand alone, get with someone.
We're gonna have a party in this place.
Let the music fill the air,
let joy and laughter lift your cares,
we're gonna have a party in this place,
we're gonna have a party in this place.

Time to be happy, let me hear you
shout:
dancing with friends, let your joy
break out.
Jesus is amongst us, he loves to see
you smile.
Leave your sadness and be happy for
a while,
happy for a while.

Wave the banners, ribbons too:
God wants his joy to flow through you.
We're gonna have a party in this place.
Don't hold back or live in fear,
there's room for young and old ones here,
we're gonna have a party in this place,
we're gonna have a party in this place.

336 Unknown

The wise man built his house upon
    the rock,
the wise man built his house upon
    the rock,
the wise man built his house upon
    the rock,
and the rain came tumbling down.
And the rain came down and the floods
    came up,
the rain came down and the floods
    came up,
the rain came down and the floods
    came up,
and the house on the rock stood firm.

The foolish man built his house upon
  the sand,
the foolish man built his house upon
  the sand,
the foolish man built his house upon
  the sand,
and the rain came tumbling down.
And the rain came down and the floods
  came up,
the rain came down and the floods
  came up,
the rain came down and the floods
  came up,
and the house on the sand fell flat.

337 Paul Field

The women went to Jesus' tomb
on that Easter day,
they found an angel had been there
to roll the stone away.

  Roll the stone, roll the stone,
  roll the stone away.
  The angel came on Easter day
  to roll the stone away.

They found that Jesus was alive,
and still he lives today,
for God has raised him from the dead,
and rolled the stone away.

Don't let your heart be like a tomb,
empty, dark and grey,
trust in Jesus, he's the rock
to roll your stone away.

Last chorus
  Roll the stone, roll the stone,
  roll the stone away.

Trust in Jesus, he's the rock
to roll your stone away.
Trust in Jesus, he's the rock
to roll your stone away.

338 Capt. Alan Price, CA

The word of the Lord is planted in my
  heart
and I want to see it grow.
The word of the Lord is planted in my
  heart
and I want you to know,
I won't let the enemy take it,
or let bad times shake it;
I won't let other things choke it out
  (choke, choke, choke),
'cos I want to let it grow, grow, grow,
'cos I want to let it grow!
(yeah!)

339 Capt. Alan Price, CA

This is a catchy songa, we sing it to the
  conga,
we dance and sing to Christ the King.
Why don't you sing alonga, while we
  dance the conga,
praise God above for all his love.

King David danced before the Lord,
worship filled his heart;
we can dance before him, too,
this is how we start . . .

Jesus is the greatest friend,
alive for us today,
he said, 'I'm with you 'till the end,
I'm with you all the way!'

340 Capt. Alan Price, CA

This is a song for the children of the Lord,
a simple song to our King.
A song of happiness and simple faith,
our praise and thanks we bring.

This is a dance for the children of the Lord,
a simple dance for our King.
A dance of happiness and simple faith,
our praise and thanks we bring.

Lai, lai, lai, . . .

© 1996 Daybreak Music Ltd

341 Les Garrett

This is the day,
this is the day that the Lord has made,
that the Lord has made;
we shall rejoice,
we shall rejoice and be glad in it,
and be glad in it.
This is the day that the Lord has made,
we shall rejoice and be glad in it;
this is the day,
this is the day that the Lord has made.

© 1967 Scripture in Song/Integrity Music/Sovereign Music UK

342 Paul Field

This is the nose God chose for me,
and I suppose that you can see,
there's no one in the world with a nose
    like me,
thank you, Lord.
(Repeat)

Thank you, Lord,
because we know it's true,
all these diff'rent faces,
look beautiful to you.

These are the ears God chose for me,
and I suppose that you can see,
there's no one in the world with ears
    like me,
thank you, Lord.
(Repeat)

This is the mouth God chose for me,
and I suppose that you can see,
there's no one in the world with a mouth
    like me,
thank you, Lord.
(Repeat)

These are the eyes God chose for me,
and I suppose that you can see,
there's no one in the world with eyes
    like me,
thank you, Lord.
(Repeat)

© 1997 Daybreak Music Ltd

343 Ernie Rettino and Debbie Kerner Rettino

This little light of mine, I'm gonna let it
    shine.
This little light of mine, I'm gonna let it
    shine.
This little light of mine, I'm gonna let it
    shine.
Ev'ry day, ev'ry day, ev'ry day in ev'ry way.
I'm gonna let my little light shine.
(Repeat)

On a Monday, he gave me the gift of love.
On a Tuesday, his peace came down
    from above.
On a Wednesday, he told me just what
    to say.
On a Thursday, he told me just how to
    pray.
On a Friday, he gave me a little more faith.

On a Saturday, he gave me a lot more
   grace.
On a Sunday, he gave me the power
   divine
to let my little light shine.

344 Capt. Alan Price, CA

Three little words that mean so much,
'God loves me!'
Three little words that deeply touch me,
'God loves me!'
I know it, 'cos God said it,
and he would never lie.
I know it, 'cos he showed it,
when he sent his Son to die for me.
Three little words that mean so much,
'God loves me!'

Three little words I mean so much, Lord,
'I love you!'
Three little words I want to tell you,
'I love you!'
You know that when I say it,
I'm trying to be real.
You know that when I say it,
it's not just when I feel you love me.
Three little words I want to tell you,
'I love you!'

345 C. C. Kerr

Two little eyes to look to God,
two little ears to hear his word,
two little feet to walk in his ways,
two little lips to sing his praise,
two little hands to do his will,
and one little heart to love him still.

346 Sammy Horner

*Uh well, it's excellent to be obedient,
   u-hu-hu!*
*Uh well, it's excellent to be obedient,
   u-hu-hu!*
*You don't say 'no' to your ma and pa;
   you say 'u-hu'.*

Uh well, it ain't real good to be real
   rude, no, no, no.
Uh well, it ain't real good to be real
   rude, no, no, no.
You've gotta treat your parents like you
   know you should, u-hu-hu!

It don't show aptitude to have an
   attitude, no, no, no.
It don't show aptitude to have an
   attitude, no, no, no.
You've gotta treat your parents like you
   know you should, u-hu-hu!

347 Paul Field

Up, down, turn around,
touch your head, touch the ground,
left, right, side to side,
legs together, legs astride,
stand up straight, touch your toes,
squeeze your tum, pinch your nose.
Up, down, turn around,
clap your hands and shout (all right!)
(Repeat)

Fit for life, in body and in mind.
Fit for life, to live for Jesus all the time.
Up, down, turn, around, clap your hands
   and shout (yeah!)

348 Capt. Alan Price, CA

Up, up, up and away!
We're taking off as we follow Jesus.
Up, up, up and away!
We're moving on with God.

Our luggage packed and our ticket
  in hand,
we come to Jesus and we understand
that he paid a great price, even willing
  to die.
When we know we're forgiven it's as if
  we can fly!

His Spirit's fuel gives the power we need
for ev'ry word, and for ev'ry deed,
and a beacon is there to guide us along,
his word is the Bible, shows what's right
  and what's wrong.

349 Jim Bailey

We are kingdom kids, kids of the
  kingdom.
We let Jesus Christ be number one in
  our lives.
We are kingdom kids, kids of the
  kingdom.
We're gonna serve our God and King.

Jesus Christ is alive, reigning with the
  Father,
we're gonna let his will be done on earth.
Putting Jesus first, for the Spirit of God
  we thirst,
singing to Jesus for all he's worth.

Whatever we do, Jesus it's for you,
we want you to completely be our Lord.
You came and gave your life, and so it's
  only right,
we should love you more and more.

350 Traditional South African. Translation (verse 1) Anders Nyberg, (verses 2 and 3) Andrew Maries

We are marching in the light of God,
we are marching in the light of God.
We are marching in the light of God,
we are marching in the light of God.

We are marching, marching,
we are marching, oh,
we are marching in the light of God.
(Repeat)

We are living in the love of God . . .

We are moving in the pow'r of God . . .

Optional traditional South African words

Siyahamb' ekukhanyen' kwenkhos',
siyahamb' ekukhanyen' kwenkhos'.
Siyahamb' ekukhanyen' kwenkhos',
siyahamb' ekukhanyen' kwenkhos'.

Siyahamba, hamba,
siyahamba, hamba,
siyahamb' ekukhanyen' kwenkhos'.
(Repeat)

351 Ian Smale

We are one, we are family together,
'cause we've one Father caring for us all.
We are one, we are related to each
  other;
Lord, help me to love my family much
  more.

352 Capt. Alan Price, CA

We are the Lord's kids, his kids,
special kids, chosen kids,
big kids, little kids, following the Lord.
(Repeat)

Though we may be small,
Jesus wants us all;
an army for the Lord,
living by his Word.
(Repeat)

However old we are,
we can know his pow'r;
whoever we may be,
Jesus is the key.
(Repeat)

The way we think, the way we act,
the enemy we'll fight!
At school, at home, at work, at play,
we'll learn to do what's right.
(Repeat)

353 Ian Smale

We believe in Hebrews thirteen, eight,
Jesus Christ is never out of date.
If it's yesterday or today, or for evermore,
Jesus stays the same and that is great.

354 Sammy Horner

We don't believe the devil's lie,
we will shout our battle cry.
Though we may be very small,
Jesus Christ is Lord of all.
He's good for me, he's good for you.
He's good for me, good for our whole
  church.

When temptation comes our way,
this is what we're gonna say:
'Don't you come and mess with me,
in Jesus' name our victory.
In Jesus' name our victory.
In Jesus' name our victory.'

Jesus is the King of kings,
he's the Lord of ev'rything.
If Satan comes, here's what we say:
'In Jesus' name, now go away.
Now go away, in Jesus' name!
Now go away, in Jesus' name!
Now go away, in Jesus' name!'

355 Paul Crouch and David Mudie

We don't sing songs just for
  ourselves,
we sing them for our King,
and if we really mean it,
then he loves it when we sing.

So we clap our hands (clap),
stamp our feet (stamp),
jump up and down (boing boing),
touch our toes (oh!),
and sing them for our King,
sing them for our King,
sing them for our King,
sing them for our King.

We don't sing songs to please our
  friends,
we sing them for our King,
and if we really mean it,
then he loves it when we sing.

356 Geoffrey Gardner

Welcome, welcome,
we're glad that you have come;
welcome, welcome,
from each and ev'ry one.

Welcome, welcome,
we're glad that you belong;
welcome, welcome,
from each and ev'ry one.

357 Debby Kerner

Welcome to the family,
we're glad that you have come
to share your life with us,
as we grow in love;
and may we always be to you
what God would have us be,
a family always there,
to be strong and to lean on.
May we learn to love each other
more with each new day,
may words of love be on our lips
in ev'rything we say.
May the Spirit melt our hearts
and teach us how to pray,
that we might be a true family.

358 Capt. Alan Price, CA

We'll sing this song for you,
a birthday song for you,
we'll sing this song for you today.
May Jesus be with you
in ev'rything you do,
this is our birthday pray'r
for you today.
(Repeat)

Happy birthday! Happy birthday!
Happy birthday to you!

359 Capt. Alan Price, CA

*We need to grow, grow, grow, grow,
grow in the grace of the Saviour,
we need to grow, grow, grow, grow,
grow in the knowledge of Jesus our
Lord.**
(Repeat)

We'll grow as we pray to him,
spend some time each day.
We'll grow as we worship him,
give him our love and praise!

We grow as we read of him
and the way for us to live;
we'll grow as we work for him,
as our lives to him we give.

We grow as we learn and share
with others that we know;
these are the things to do
if we really want to grow.

* Last time
*We need to grow in the knowledge of
Jesus our Lord.*

360 Capt. Alan Price, CA

We praise God in the morning when the
sun is bright,
we praise him in the evening when day
turns to night.
We praise him if it's sunny or if it's wet.
No matter what the weather we'll never
forget to

*praise God (bop, bop, showaddy do
    wah).
Praise God (bop, bop, showaddy do
    wah).
Hallelujah, we'll praise the Lord.*

We praise God when we're singing our
    songs of praise,
we praise him when we worship in our
    different ways,
we praise him for the food that we eat
    each day,
but in everything we do we want to say,

© 1994 Daybreak Music Ltd

361 Capt. Alan Price, CA

We praise you, Jesus, we praise you, Jesus,
we just want to let you know.
We praise you, Jesus, we praise you, Jesus,
when you came so long ago.
You came to save us,
new life you gave us,
when you died upon the cross.
And that's the reason that we're believin'
that you really care for us!

© 1990 Daybreak Music Ltd

362 Capt. Alan Price, CA

We're a bright light together,
with the light of Jesus we shine;
we're a grand band together,
with our friend Jesus it's fine.
We're a swell smell together,
it's the fragrance of Jesus we share!
Whenever we are together,
Jesus is specially there.
Even before time began,
we were part of God's great plan;
'cos of Jesus we would be
part of his great family!

© 1991 Daybreak Music Ltd

363 Capt. Alan Price, CA

We're going to praise the Lord,
we're going to praise the Lord,
we're going to praise the Lord,
for he is good!
We're going to praise the Lord,
we're going to praise the Lord,
we're going to praise the Lord,
for he is good!

We'll praise him with our shouts of
    praise
(oggie, oggie, oggie, oy, oy, oy);
we'll praise him in more normal ways
(hallelujah! hallelu);
we'll praise him by the way we live
(stand up, stand up for Jesus);
we'll praise him in the way we give
(time and money, time and money).
More than anything else we do,
Lord, we give our praise to you!

© 1998 Daybreak Music Ltd

364 Andrew and Pauline Pearson

We wanna sing about your love
and tell ev'ryone we know.
Let it change our lives
so that we can let it show.
Father, we receive your love
that comes from knowing you,
as we enjoy your love,
help us show love to others too.

*Let your love pour into our lives,
    O Lord,
let your love pour into our lives.
Let your love pour into our lives,
    O Lord,
let your love pour into our lives.*

Continued overleaf

We wanna sing about your love
and tell ev'ryone we know.
Let it change our lives
so that we can let it show.
Jesus we receive the joy
that comes from knowing you.
The way you gave your life,
help us to offer ours to you.

Let your joy pour into our lives,
O Lord,
let your joy pour into our lives.
Let your joy pour into our lives,
O Lord,
let your joy pour into our lives.

We wanna sing about your love
and tell ev'ryone we know.
Let it change our lives
so that we can let it show.
Spirit we receive the pow'r
that comes from knowing you.
Will you change our lives,
so we can be of use to you?

Let your power pour into our lives . . .

© 1997 Daybreak Music Ltd

365 Doug Horley

We want to see Jesus lifted high,
a banner that flies across this land,
that all men might see the truth
and know he is the way to heaven.
(Repeat)

We want to see, we want to see,
we want to see Jesus lifted high.
We want to see, we want to see,
we want to see Jesus lifted high.

Step by step we're moving forward,
little by little taking ground,
ev'ry prayer a powerful weapon,
strongholds come tumbling down,
and down, and down, and down.

We want to see Jesus . . .

We're gonna see . . .

© 1993 Kingsway's Thankyou Music

366 Kath Hall

We will turn the hearts of the fathers
so they will look again to their children.
We will turn the hearts of the children
so that together we can look to you.
(Repeat)

The young and the old now,
standing together,
looking to Jesus to carry us through.
All diff'rent races, all diff'rent ages,
all of us here for your glory.
And we call on your Spirit,
keep us together and pour in your power.

The walls have been broken,
we stand as one now,
one in the Spirit and won by your blood.
We're moving forwards under your banner,
telling the world of your glory.
And we take on your promise,
together we'll welcome the Day of
the Lord!

© 1996 Chasah Music/Daybreak Music Ltd

367 Capt. Alan Price, CA

We worship you, Father, Son and Holy
Spirit;
believe in you, Holy Trinity.
We follow you, Father, Son and Holy
Spirit;
Almighty God, Holy Trinity.

God the Father, God the Son,
and Holy Spirit too;
each is God, yet God is One,
the Bible says it's true.

I don't pretend to understand
how this can really be,
yet by faith I know it's true,
this holy mystery.

368 Mick Gisbey

What a whale of a tale when Jonah sailed
out on the ocean blue:
God spoke that day, but he ran away
from what he was told to do;
and out on a boat that could hardly float,
on a rough and stormy sea,
the sailors asked: 'Whose fault is this?'
and Jonah piped up: 'Me!'

It doesn't pay to disobey,
for what God said is right;
don't try to hide, God sees inside
so don't put up a fight.
(Repeat)

369 Lucy East

All What noise shall we make to say
that God is great?
What noise shall we make unto
the Lord?
Leader Let's make a loud noise to say
that God is great.
Let's make a loud noise unto the
Lord.
All Here is my loud noise:
Here is my loud noise:
Here is my loud noise unto the
Lord.

Let's make a quiet noise . . .

Let's make a fast noise . . .

Let's make a slow noise . . .

Let's make a joyful noise . . .

Let's make a praising noise . . .
Here is my praising noise: God is good!

We love making noise
to say that God is great.
We love making noise
unto the Lord.

370 Mary Wright

What was it like for the shepherds,
out on the hills in the night?
What was it like for the shepherds,
on seeing the bright, shining light?

(Shout) *Hear the angels!*

Glory! Glory! Glory to God on high!
Glory! Glory! Glory to God on high!

What was it like for the shepherds,
seeing an angel out there?
What was it like for the shepherds,
so scared by the sudden bright glare?

What was it like for the shepherds,
leaving their sheep in the cold?
What was it like for the shepherds
to do as the angel had told?

There was great joy for the shepherds,
leaving their fields cold and wild!
There was great joy for the shepherds,
on seeing the newly born child.

371 Jan Struther

When a knight won his spurs, in the
　　stories of old,
he was gentle and brave he was gallant
　　and bold;
with a shield on his arm and a lance in
　　his hand,
for God and for valour he rode through
　　the land.

No charger have I, and no sword by my
　　side,
yet still to adventure and battle I ride,
though back into storyland giants have
　　fled,
and the knights are no more and the
　　dragons are dead.

Let faith be my shield and let joy be my
　　steed
'gainst the dragons of anger, the ogres
　　of greed;
and let me set free, with the sword of
　　my youth
for the castle of darkness, the pow'r of
　　the truth.

© Oxford University Press

372 Capt. Alan Price, CA

Whenever I'm afraid, I will trust in Jesus,
whenever I'm afraid, I will trust in him.
Whenever I'm afraid, I will trust in Jesus,
whenever I'm afraid, I will trust in him.

When I'm alone, I know he's there,
when it's dark, I know he's near,
when I am hurt, I know he cares,
I know he's bigger than all my fears.

© 1998 Daybreak Music Ltd

373 Capt. Alan Price, CA

When I am hurt in the daily fight
to live for Jesus and do what is right,
I'll find a quiet place, and then I'll pray
and ask God to heal what's been
　　damaged that day.

I'll ask his forgiveness for things I've
　　done wrong,
and breathe in his Spirit once more to
　　be strong;
and so I'll be ready to face a new day,
with ev'ry new challenge that may come
　　my way.

© 1998 Daybreak Music Ltd

374 Rosie Jarvis

When I look at the trees,
blowing in the breeze,
oo, I praise you,
oo, I praise you.
When I see a bird up high,
swooping in the sky,
oo, I praise you,
oo, I praise you.

　　It's a wonderful world for boys and
　　　　girls,
　　such a wonderful world for boys and
　　　　girls,
　　and we praise you, Creator God.

When I feel the gentle rain,
splashing down again,
oo, I praise you,
oo, I praise you.
When I touch the golden sand,
spreading it with my hand,
oo, I praise you,
oo, I praise you.

When I see the silver stars,
sparkling in the skies,
oo, I praise you,
oo, I praise you.

375 Dave Bird and Sarah Lacy

When I'm in bed and it's night,
I don't want mum to turn out the light,
because there might be giants or things
that frighten, or monsters looking at me.
But when I'm shaking down to my
     knees,
seeing the shadows up in the trees,
I will remember you are my friend
and I will be fine, just listen to me!

*'Cause I've got a friend who's bigger
     than that,
he never leaves me whatever I'm at;
there is no need for fear 'cause you
     are here,
oh Jesus, you're all that I need.
Whenever I call you, you're already here,
and you always listen whatever my fear,
and I want to know you more and now
I'm sure that friends for ever we'll be.*

There's a boy in the class above me,
and he's so much bigger than me,
and I don't want to go to the
     playground,
'cause I'm scared of what he'd do to me!

But I've got a friend . . .

And when I'm feeling sad and alone,
and all the other kids have gone home,
then I can pray and call out your name
and I'll know that you are with me once
     more.

And I've got a friend . . .

376 Mark and Helen Johnson

When I think about the cross,
when I think of Jesus,
I'm reminded of his love,
love that never leaves me.
Who am I that he should die,
giving life so freely?
(Repeat)

Last time
When I think about the cross,
help me to believe it.

377 Nigel Hemming

When there is nowhere to turn,
when there is no one who cares,
when I am feeling afraid and alone,
my Jesus will always be there.

I know I'm his precious child.
I know he's my special friend.
I know that I'll always be safe in his love,
as I give him my heart once again.

378 Joe King

When there's hard times or there's good
     times,
when the rain falls or the sun shines,
when you test me or you bless me,
my resolve will none the less be:

*I will love you come what may,
I will love you ev'ry day;
I will love you now and for evermore.*

Continued overleaf

When there's dark clouds or there's clear
    skies,
when it's sunset or it's sunrise,
when I'm needy or I've plenty,
Lord, not one thing will prevent me:

I will love you come what may,
I will love you ev'ry day;
I will love you now and for evermore.

When your presence seems so distant,
when my doubts seem so persistent,
then no matter how I'm feeling,
Lord, in one thing I'm unyielding:

When the battle seems so endless,
when I'm feeling so defenceless,
when the enemy surrounds me
and his arrows fly around me:

When my future is uncertain,
when my heart is heavy-burdened,
when I'm tired or I'm hurting,
Lord, in one thing I'm determined:

When the past seems to pursue me,
when temptation whispers to me,
when my worst fears are awakened,
Lord, on one thing I'm unshaken:

379 Capt. Alan Price, CA

When the time is right,
whether day or night,
the Lord Jesus Christ will come again
(he'll come again).
As we wait for that day,
in our work and our play,
we'll let our light shine bright
and live for the King who will reign.

380 Capt. Alan Price, CA

When we're together with Jesus
and we happily sing his songs,
it's easy to be his follower,
it's good to know we belong;
but at other times it can be so hard
to do what's right and good.
When those around don't know the
    Lord,
and don't live as they should.
O Lord, keep me strong,
never to deny you.
O Lord, when it's hard,
help me to keep by you.

381 Mike Burn

When you pray, go into your own room;
when you pray, close the door.
(Repeat)

Pray to Father, who is unseen,
and your Father, who sees what you do,
he'll reward you.

When you pray, don't use lots of long
    words,
when you pray, as some people do.
They think if their prayers go on for
    ages,
God will hear, but that isn't true.

For your Father already knows,
yes, your Father, he knows what you
    need
and will answer.

382 Paul Field and Ralph Chambers

When you're feeling good, put your
    thumbs up.
When you're feeling bad, put them down.
When you're feeling happy you can smile
    all day.
When you're feeling low, wear a frown;
but don't just follow your feelings,
trust in God and his Word.
No matter what you feel, put your
    thumbs up,
put your faith in the Lord.

383 Capt. Alan Price, CA

Wherever he rules, it's good when he is
    in charge,
it's best when we do as he says,
    it pleases God:
let Jesus Christ be 'Number One' in our
    lives.
(Repeat)

For the Son of God is the King of
    hearts,
who rules with love, truth and justice;
and we will speak his words and do his
    deeds,
by the pow'r of the Spirit he gives us!

Wherever he rules, it's good when he is
    in charge,
it's best when we do as he says, it
    pleases God:
let Jesus Christ be 'Number One' in our
    lives.
Let Jesus Christ be 'Number One',
Jesus Christ be 'Number One',
Jesus Christ be 'Number One' in our
    lives!

384 Graham Kendrick

Whether you're one or whether you're two
or three or four or five,
six or sev'n or eight or nine,
it's good to be alive.
It really doesn't matter how old you are,
Jesus loves you whoever you are.

La la la la la la la la, la,
Jesus loves us all.
La la la la la la la la, la,
Jesus loves us all.

Whether you're big or whether you're
    small,
or somewhere in between,
first in the class or middle or last,
we're all the same to him.
It really doesn't matter how clever you are,
Jesus loves you whoever you are.

385 Unknown

Who made the twinkling stars,
the twinkling stars, the twinkling stars?
Who made the twinkling stars?
Our Father God.

Who made the birds that fly,
the birds that fly, the birds that fly?
Who made the birds that fly?
Our Father God.

Who made the rolling seas,
the rolling seas, the rolling seas?
Who made the rolling seas?
Our Father God.

Who made both you and me,
you and me, you and me?
Who made both you and me?
Our Father God.

386 Paul Booth

Who put the colours in the rainbow?
Who put the salt into the sea?
Who put the cold into the snowflake?
Who made you and me?
Who put the hump upon the camel?
Who put the neck on the giraffe?
Who put the tail upon the monkey?
Who made hyenas laugh?
Who made whales and snails and quails?
Who made hogs and dogs and frogs?
Who made bats and rats and cats?
Who made ev'rything?

Who put the gold into the sunshine?
Who put the sparkle in the stars?
Who put the silver in the moonlight?
Who made Earth and Mars?
Who put the scent into the roses?
Who taught the honey bees to dance?
Who put the tree inside the acorn?
It surely can't be chance!
Who made seas and leaves and trees?
Who made snow and winds that blow?
Who made streams and rivers flow?
God made all of these!

387 Mark and Helen Johnson

Who spoke words of wisdom and life?
Only the one they call Jesus.
Understood what people are like?
Nobody other than him.
Who performed miraculous signs?
Only the one they call Jesus.
Healed the sick, gave sight to the blind?
Nobody other than him.

Hosanna! Hosanna!
Praise him! Come praise him!
Hosanna! Hosanna!
Lift up your voices and sing!

Who took children into his arms?
Only the one they call Jesus.
Spoke to storms and made them calm?
Nobody other than him.
Who raised Lazarus from the dead?
Only the one they call Jesus.
Made a feast of fishes and bread?
Nobody other than him.

Who made friends with people
    despised?
Only the one they call Jesus.
Turned the water into good wine?
Nobody other than him.
Who got people following him?
Only the one they call Jesus.
Changed their lives, forgave all their sin?
Nobody other than him.

388 Unknown

Who's the king of the jungle?
Who's the king of the sea?
Who's the king of the universe,
and who's the king of me?
I'll tell you: J - E - S - U - S is,
he's the king of me;
he's the king of the universe,
the jungle and the sea.

389 Paul Herbert

Who taught the spider to spin his web?
Who spoke the first words ever said?
Who put the waves in the deep blue sea?
Who knows all there is about me, me, me?
My Father.

My Father is big, he's strong and he's
  tough,
I know that he cares, his word I trust.
Whenever I fall, he helps me to stand.
My Father holds me secure in his
  hand.

Who taught the bird to sing her song?
Who drew the line between right and
  wrong?
Who paints the rainbow across the sky?
Who will hear me when I cry, cry, cry?
My Father.

390 Capt. Alan Price, CA

Why is it me? Why is it me?
Why do all the things like this happen
  to me?
Why is it me? Why is it me?
Isn't there someone else other than me?

Ananias heard the Lord call him one day,
'I've got a job for you to do straight
  away.
Find a house in Straight Street and ask
  for a man,
his name is Saul of Tarsus, now be quick
  as you can.'

'This Saul had a vision and it's going to
  come true,
he's seen a man lay hands on him, and
  that man is you!'
Ananais was worried, 'cos he'd heard
  about Saul,
he'd caused trouble for believers – he
  wasn't nice at all!
Oh . . .

God said, 'Go, Ananias, and do what I
  ask,
I've chosen this Saul for a special task.'
Ananias knew that he had to obey,
he knew that he could trust the Lord,
  come what may.
But . . .

He went and found the house and laid
  his hands on Saul,
the Holy Spirit came with power – it
  didn't hurt at all.
God asks hard things even now – and of
  children too.
Don't miss the adventure, it could
  happen to you!
Oh . . .

Last Chorus
  Could it be me? Could it be me?
  How could anything like this happen
    to me?
  Could it be me? Could it be me?
  Though there may be someone else, it
    could be me.

391 Tim Moyler and the children of ICHTHUS, Beckenham

You are the best,
better than all the rest;
Jesus you're the best.
You are the best,
better than all the rest;
Jesus you're the best.

Thank you, Lord, for giving us
our food and drink each day.
When we're sick you heal us with your
  love.
Lord, we love to praise you,
for you love and care for us.
We want to get to know you more each
  day.

392 Chris Jackson

You are the Light of the world,
I won't walk in darkness.
You are the Way, the Truth and the Life,
I'm gonna follow you.

You are the good, Good Shepherd,
you take care of me.
You are the Resurrection and the Life,
I'm gonna live with you.

You are the Bread of Life,
I will not be hungry.
You are the Vine and I am the branch,
I will abide in you.

You are the great I AM,
who was and is and is to come.

© 1998 Powerpack/Learning Curve Music

393 Ralph Chambers

You can't catch a plane to take you to
   heaven,
not even a spaceship can get that far.
You can't take a hovercraft or helicopter
   journey,
or drive in the fastest racing car.
Only Jesus, only Jesus, only Jesus is the
   way.
Only Jesus, only Jesus, only Jesus is the
   way.

© 1991 Daybreak Music Ltd

394 Bev Gammon

*You give me joy, such a bubbly joy
that no one else can give me.
You give me joy, such a bubbly joy
that no one else can give me.*

I want to dance and run around,
I want to shout your name out loud,
'cos you give me joy, such a bubbly joy
that no one else can give me.

I want to laugh and clap my hands,
I want to praise you through the land,
'cos you give me joy, such a bubbly joy
that no one else can give me.

© 1990 Kingsway's Thankyou Music

395 Capt. Alan Price, CA

You lift your left arm high, your left arm
   high,
your left arm straight up, wave it in the
   sky.
You raise your arm to Jesus as you sing
   God's praise,
it's the Holy Hokey for God!

   *Give the glory to the Father,
   give the glory to the Son,
   give the glory to the Spirit,
   our great God 'Three in One'
   Amen!*

You lift your right arm high, your right
   arm high,
your right arm straight up, wave it in the
   sky.
You raise your arm to Jesus as you sing
   God's praise,
it's the Holy Hokey for God!

You lift your left arm high, your right
   arm high,
both arms straight up, wave them in
   the sky.
You raise your arms to Jesus as you sing
   God's praise,
it's the Holy Hokey for God!

You lift your face up high, your face up
    high,
lift your face up, gazing to the sky.
You're looking up to Jesus as you sing
    God's praise,
it's the Holy Hokey for God!

396   Mark and Helen Johnson

You may be happy, you may be sad,
you may be pretty or plain;
you may be skinny or getting fat,
maybe you wish you could change.

You may be wealthy, you may be poor,
you may be scruffy or smart;
but love is real when you know for sure,
it takes you just as you are.

If we're right or we're wrong,
if we're weak or we're strong,
if we're winning or losing a game;
whether black or white skin,
with a frown or a grin,
well, the Lord loves us all just the
same.

They say to copy the TV stars,
they say 'Keep up with the trends';
to have the fashions and look the part,
just like the rest of your friends.

They say 'Try harder', they say 'Perform',
they say 'Do things to impress';
but love is real when you know for sure,
it won't depend on success.

397   Mick Gisbey

You may think I'm so young, too young
    to understand;
don't forget, in God's eyes, he looks on
    me as grand.
He never, never limits the giant that's in
    me;
he leads me through my childhood,
    supernaturally.

I'm not a grasshopper, I'm a giant in the
    Lord.
I'm not a grasshopper, I'm a giant in the
    Lord.
(Repeat)

398   Ian Smale

You never put a light under a dirty old
    bucket.
You never put your light under a dirty
    old bucket.
You never put your light under a dirty
    old bucket
if you want light to shine around, round,
    round.
Shine, shine around, round, round.
Shine, shine around, round, round.
Shine a light that ev'ryone can see.
Lord, help me let my little light shine,
not just Sundays, all the time,
so friends give praise to you when they
    see me.

399 Ian White

Your name is Jesus, your love is true;
you ask your children to come to you,
to learn to follow, your Spirit's ways,
and with our whole lives bring you
    praise.

© 1991 Little Misty Music/Kingsway's Thankyou Music

400 Ian White

You say the harvest is plentiful,
but workers are few,
Lord, I am ready and willing
just to follow you.
(Repeat)

I'll listen and I'll pray
for what your Spirit says,
and I'll begin to look
inside your Holy Book.

I'll stay here in my street,
I'll tell the people I meet,
about Lord Jesus Christ,
who set me free inside.

I'll go to Africa,
I'll go to India,
wherever you send me,
that's where I want to be.

© 1987 Little Misty Music/Kingsway's Thankyou Music

401 Carey Landry

A butterfly, **a butterfly**,
an Easter egg, **an Easter egg**,
a fountain flowing in the park,
a fountain flowing in the park

These are signs of new life;
the life of Jesus the Lord.
And we sing to him, alleluia!
We give to him our praise!
We sing to him, alleluia!
Glory be to him! *Glory be to him!*
Glory be to Jesus the Lord!

A helping hand, **a helping hand**,
a happy smile, **a happy smile**,
a heart so full of hope and joy,
a heart so full of hope and joy.

A cup of wine, **a cup of wine**,
a loaf of bread, **a loaf of bread**,
blest and broken for us,
blest and broken for us.

© 1979 Carey Landry/NALR

402 James Wright

All around the world, all around the
    world,
people are celebrating Christmas,
people are giving thanks to God.
All around the world, all around the
    world,
people are celebrating Christmas, all
    around the world.

From the United Kingdom to Australia
to the shores of Brazil,
from the land of China to South Africa,
to the streets of Seville.
All over the USA, Philadelphia to L.A.
Ev'ry nation, ev'ry tribe and tongue
come, give him praise.

From the Middle East to Indonesia
to the shores of Japan,
from Columbia to Yugoslavia,
to the streets of Sudan.
All over the world today
people celebrate this special day.
Ev'ry country, ev'ry tribe and tongue
come, give him praise.

Celebrate,
lift your hearts and sing as one.
Celebrate,
ev'ry nation, ev'ry tongue,
the coming of the Holy One
all around the world.
(Repeat)

Let the people rejoice
all around the world,
ev'ry tribe, ev'ry tongue,
all around the world.
(Repeat)

© 2002 Kevin Mayhew Ltd.

403 Susan Sayers

All of the people on the mountain,
all of the people in the valley,
all of the people in the villages and
the town,
say to each other on the way,
'Bring all your friends and don't delay,
Jesus of Nazareth is coming here
today.'

Jesus, Jesus, when we are with you,
it's strange, and yet it's true,
we start to feel that there is
more to life than living as we do.
It's richer and more satisfying
than we ever knew.

Jesus, Jesus, healing as you go,
your loving seems to flow
like water from a fountain,
and as we are touched we want to grow
in love towards each other –
just because you love us so!

Jesus, Jesus, we have come to see
that you must really be
the Son of God our Father.
We've been with you and we all agree
that only in your service
can the world be truly free!

© 1986 Kevin Mayhew Ltd.

404 Pamela Dew

And God said,
'Let there be light in my new world
where night gives way to each new day.'
And God looked at the light that he had
    made
and he saw that it was good.

And God said,
'Let there be space in my new world,
a sky of blue, the deep sea too.'
And God looked at the space that he
    had made
and he saw that it was good.

And God said,
'Let there be plants in my new world,
with flow'rs and leaves and fruits and
    seeds.'
And God looked at the plants that he
    had made
and he saw that they were good.

Continued overleaf

And God said,
'Let there be stars in my new world
the sunshine bright, the moon by night.'
And God looked at the stars that he had
  made
and he saw that they were good.

And God said,
'Let there be creatures in my new world
to run, swim, fly and multiply.'
And God looked at the creatures he had
  made
and he saw that they were good.

And God said,
'Let there be people in my new world,
I'd like to share my world so fair.'
And God said to the people living there,
'Now it's your world too, so please take
  care
of all living kinds, both great and small;
I love them all.'

405 Andy Read

And I will worship you,
Lord, I sing it with my heart.
And I will worship you,
never let me be apart
from all your holy ways
for I know that they are good,
so teach me how to stay
close beside you all the way.
And I will love you, and I will serve you,
and I will follow all my days.
(Repeat)

406 James Montgomery

Angels from the realms of glory,
wing your flight o'er all the earth;
ye who sang creation's story
now proclaim Messiah's birth:

Come and worship,
Christ, the new-born King;
come and worship,
worship Christ, the new-born King.

Shepherds, in the field abiding,
watching o'er your flocks by night,
God with us is now residing,
yonder shines the infant Light:

Sages, leave your contemplations;
brighter visions beam afar:
seek the great Desire of Nations;
ye have seen his natal star:

Saints before the altar bending,
watching long in hope and fear,
suddenly the Lord, descending,
in his temple shall appear:

Though an infant now we view him,
he shall fill his Father's throne,
gather all the nations to him;
ev'ry knee shall then bow down:

407 Dave Godfrey

Anyone who hears his words,
and does just what he says,
is like the man who built upon the rock.
Oh, the rain came tumblin' down,
  streams rose,
mighty wind did roar,
his house stood strong, ace foundations.
Wise man!

He's my ace foundation,
my ace foundation,
I will build my life on him!
He's my ace foundation, my ace
  foundation,
I will build my life on Jesus,
and what he says to me!

Anyone who hears his words,
ignores just what he says,
is like the man who built upon the sand.
Oh, the rain came tumblin' down,
    streams rose,
the mighty wind did roar,
his house went crash – no foundations.
Foolish man! But he's my …

409 Ian Smale

As I look around me, this is what I see,
boys and girls made as God made them
    to be.
I must love them more than I love me.
Singing, hi diddle de hi hi,
ho diddle de ho ho,
hi diddle de ho, diddle de dum, diddle
    de de.

408 Andy Pickford

Are you wired up to the pow'r of the
    Lord?
Are you wired up to sing his praise
    aloud?
Are you wired up, as we sing this
    song,
to our wonderful, powerful God?

You're the maker of all things,
you made the stars that shine:
you made the flowing rivers,
you made the mountains high.

You walked upon the water,
you made the blind to see,
you even fed five thousand:
I know you care for me.

You're our Friend and Saviour,
you're our loving King,
you're the one who died for us
and this is why we sing.

410 Roger Jones

A stranger walked along the shore of
    Galilee.
He met two fishermen, and then cried
    'Follow me!'
They left their nets, and then
he taught them to catch men.
They watched him as he died and rose
    again!
It was the King!

Worship the King!
Worship the King!
Worship the King who rules over the
    world so we sing!
Jesus is King!
Jesus is King!
Jesus is King! He rules over my life so
    I sing!

The stranger walked along the road to
    Calvary.
They nailed him to a cross of wood so
    cruelly.
The women watched and cried,
the blood flowed from his side,
the sun stopped shining as the Saviour
    died!
It was the King!

Continued overleaf

Worship the King!
Worship the King!
Worship the King who rules over the
world so we sing!
Jesus is King!
Jesus is King!
Jesus is King! He rules over my life so
I sing!

When Mary came to see the tomb, so
early,
the stone was moved, his body gone!
'Where can it be?'
A voice came from behind,
it sounded, oh, so kind,
then suddenly it dawned upon her mind –
it was the King!

411 Andrew & Wendy Rayner

As we walk the path of life,
we know that God is with us,
he loves us all the time,
God loves us all the time.
No matter how we look or feel,
his love for us is always real,
because we have this certainty
we're gonna sing this song for evermore,
we're gonna sing this song for evermore.

As we go through ev'ry day,
we know we're not alone,
he loves us all the time,
God loves us all the time.
No matter if we're old or young,
his love for us goes on and on,
because we have this certainty
we're gonna sing this song for evermore,
we're gonna sing his song for evermore.

No matter what the world may say
we know God's with us all the way;
because we have this certainty
we're gonna sing this song for evermore.
We're gonna sing his song for evermore,
sing his song for evermore,
sing his song for evermore (sing his
song for evermore),
sing his song for evermore (sing his
song for evermore).

412 Alison Moon

Be bold, be strong and sing,
to Jesus Christ our King.
Be bold, be strong and sing,
for he's Lord of ev'rything.
Be bold, be strong and sing,
for he will never leave us.
The Lord is near, we need not fear,
there's power in his name.

God sent his Son to die that we might
know
just how much he cares.
He lives to give us strength and victory,
to help us through each day.

413 Susie Hare

Because I'm special to him,
no matter how bad I have been,
Jesus takes all my sin,
forgives me and washes me clean.
And he helps me become the person
that he wants to see.
I'll always love him
because he is special to me.

414 Sally-Ann Fatkin

Be first in my heart
as I seek to follow you,
be there at my side
as I trust in you.
Spirit within cries 'Lord Jesus,
be first in my heart today.'

Be first in my heart
as I choose to honour you,
be pleased with this child
as I live for you.
Spirit within cries 'Lord Jesus
be first in my heart today.'

*Then I will see with your eyes
those who are hurting,
hearing your voice.
I'll speak words of healing,
bringing your kingdom in.*

415 Mark & Helen Johnson

Before you made the skies and sea,
your heart was full of love for me.
You knew the person I would be,
thank you for loving me.

You came to earth to live like us,
with words of life, and arms of love.
You showed the way to heav'n above,
thank you for loving us.

*Thank you, Jesus, thank you, my Lord.
Your love came down from heaven,
come fill up my heart evermore.*

Because God loved the world so much
you paid the price for all of us.
You gave your life upon a cross,
thank you for loving us.

So thank you, Lord, for loving me
today and all eternity.
And may my song forever be,
thank you for loving me.

416 Chris Jackson

Be holy, be holy,
in all that you do;
be holy, be holy,
in all that you do,
just as God is holy,
God is holy,
be holy, be holy, be holy.

417 Jim Bailey

Bells, they are ringing,
children are singing,
and we are exalting the name over all.
Flags, they are dancing,
the Church is advancing,
as we are romancing the name over all.

*Jesus' kingdom can't be shaken,
Jesus' promise can't be broken,
Jesus, Lord of all creation,
name over all.
Jesus, truth of liberation,
Jesus, light of our salvation,
Jesus, only way to heaven,
the name over all.*

418 Andy Read

Best friends with you,
I wanna be best friends with Jesus.
(Repeat x4)

When I talk to you,
you can talk to me.
When I walk with you,
you can walk with me.
When I smile at you,
you can smile at me.
When I hold your hand,
you can hold mine too.

419 Chris Jackson

Be strong and courageous,
do not be terrified.
Be strong and courageous,
for the Lord is by your side.
Do not be discouraged,
do not be afraid;
for the Lord, your God, is with you
wherever you go.

420 Dave Cooke

Be strong and put on the armour of
   God.
Be strong and put on the armour of
   God.
Stand, stand, stand your ground
and in his mighty power be strong
and put on the armour of God.
(Repeat)

Put the belt of truth tightly round your
   waist.
The breast-plate of righteousness firmly
   into place.
Prepare your feet for highways broad
   and narrow.
And the shield of faith, to stop those
   burning arrows.
And on your head the helmet that will
   save us if we fall.
And the sword of the Spirit so we can
   stand up tall.

421 Susanna Levell

Be strong in the Lord and in his
   mighty pow'r,
put on the full armour of God.
Be strong in the Lord and in his
   mighty pow'r,
put on the full armour of God.

Put on the belt of truth
that will hold your armour on,
know the truth of God
and he'll help you to stay strong.
Put on the breast-plate of righteousness
to guard your very heart,
be assured of God's forgiveness
which will clean your deepest part.

Have feet of readiness
that will stand firm through the fight,
you don't want to slip and slide,
the peaceful gospel sets you right.
The shield of faith you strongly hold
which will guard you from attack,
so have faith in God alone
and nothing will you lack.

Put on the helmet of salvation
to protect your mind from doubts and
  fears
and all the things that can infect.
Now use the sword of the Spirit
for attacking in the fight,
for God's word, it makes us strong
in the power of his might.

422 Graham Kendrick

Big man standing by the blue waterside,
mending nets by the blue sea.
Along came Jesus, he said:
'Simon Peter, won't you leave your nets
  and come follow me.'

'You don't need anything, I've got
  ev'rything,
but Peter, its gonna be a hard way.
You don't have to worry now, come on
  and hurry now,
I'll walk beside you ev'ry day.'

Life wasn't easy for the big fisherman,
but still he followed till his dying day.
Along came Jesus, he said,
'Simon Peter, there's a place in heaven
  where you can stay.'

423 Steve Burnhope

Birds in the sky can flap their wings,
fish in the sea can wiggle their fins.
But they haven't got fingers
and they haven't got a chin,
so they're not like you and me.

Lions have a mighty roar,
elephants are bigger than garage doors.
But they can't just hop on one leg,
that's for sure,
so they're not like you and me.

I'm not like the animals,
no, no, no,
I've got a body and a spirit and a soul.
God made me to be diff'rent.
So I'm made in the image of God.

Grizzly bears can scratch their fleas,
chimpanzees can tickle their knees.
But they can't count up to ten quickly
like you and me.

Centipedes have got a hundred feet,
buying new shoes is a very big treat.
But they're no good at bouncing
up and down to the beat.
So they're not like you and me.

424 Dave Godfrey

Blessed are the poor in spirit:
theirs, theirs is the kingdom.
Blessed are those who mourn:
for God will comfort them!
Blessed are the humble people:
for they will inherit the earth.
Blessed are those who hunger,
thirst for the righteousness,
they will be filled.

For these are the words that I heard
  him say,
sat on a hill, he taught that day
  of blessings that his kingdom brings,
when lives reflect the glory of the King!

Continued overleaf

Blessed are the merciful:
for they will be shown mercy.
Blessed are the pure in heart:
for they will see our God.
Blessed are the peacemakers:
for they will be his children.
Blessed are the persecuted,
due to righteousness,
theirs is the kingdom!

For these are the words that I heard
him say,
sat on a hill, he taught that day
of blessings that his kingdom brings,
when lives reflect the glory of the King!

425 Andy Read

Bless the Lord,
O my soul, and all that is within me,
bless his holy name.
Bless the Lord,
O my soul, and all that is within me,
bless his holy name.

426 Steve Morgan-Gurr

Brick by brick, day by day,
I will build my life this way.
When I read, when I pray,
God will help me build.

In the Bible I can see
just how God wants me to be.
Lots of people
just like me,
God helped them to build.

How can I learn how to pray,
when I don't know what to say.
Holy Spirit, ev'ry day,
please help me to build.

427 Pamela Dew

Bring in the harvest,
share out the harvest,
God has been good to us all.
There's plenty to eat
for you and me
and the people over the sea.

Pick all the apples,
cut all the wheat down,
catch some fish from the sea.
God has been good,
God has been good,
God has been good to me.

428 Capt. Alan J. Price, CA

Building, building, ev'rybody's building:
like a building, life is what we're
building.
Building, building, ev'rybody's building
ev'ry day.
(Repeat)

In different ways, hey, hey, hey.
When we know what God has said,
and we do just what we've read,
it's like a plan. (Like a plan.)
And if we get it wrong, then it just won't
be as strong
as in the plan. (Oh man!)
Difficulties lie ahead, we don't worry, but
instead
trust in God's plan. (Jesus – God's man!)

Ev'ry day, in diff'rent ways,
hey, hey, hey.
Ev'ry day, come what may,
hey, hey, hey.

429 Phil Overton

*Call his name, Jesus, call his name,
   Saviour.
He shall save his people from their
   sins.
Call his name, Emmanuel, he came
   with us to dwell.
He'll save his people from their sins.*

Mary woke with a start one night.
A light was shining bright.
An angel was standing at her side
and he said, 'Mary, God's time has come
and you shall have a son
and he will be the Saviour of mankind.'

Mary cried, 'How can it be?
I'm only a bride to be!'
The angel said, 'Listen, I'll explain.
God's Holy Spirit will cover you.
His pow'r will overshadow you.
Your son will have a very special name.'

Now when Joseph heard the news,
he really got the blues.
He thought that Mary had been untrue
and he said, 'Right, I'm through with her'
but God said, 'Listen, sir, there's something
I'd like to say to you.'

He said 'Now Mary has found favour in
   my sight.
She hasn't been untrue, it's quite alright
for she's not the unfaithful kind of girl
and her son will be the Saviour of the
   world.'

430 Dave Cooke

C for the Christ Child born in a shed.
H is for Herod who killed the boys dead.
R for Romans who ruled the land.
I for Immanuel, God's at hand.
S for shepherds who were scared
   around ten.
T for the treasures of the three wise
   men.
M for Mary who gave birth to Jesus.
A for the angels who sang his praises.
S for the star that showed the way.
It's a song about Christmas we sing
   today.

Sing a song about Christmas,
sing a song about Christmas time.
(Repeat)

431 Christine Dalton

Chicken pox and measles,
mumps and flu.
My tummy's aching
and I feel blue.
The Bible tells us what to do:
call on Doctor Jesus.

Say 'Doctor, Doctor Jesus,
please come quick.
My tummy's aching and I feel sick.
I know prayer can do the trick;
thank you, Doctor Jesus.'

Well, if you're feeling kinda funny
and your nose is very runny,
your chicken pox are scratchy
and your face is red and patchy.
Your mumps are big and bumpy
and you're feeling kinda grumpy
here's what you should do.

Continued overleaf

Chicken pox and measles,
mumps and flu.
My tummy's aching
and I feel blue.
The Bible tells us what to do:
call on Doctor Jesus.

Say 'Doctor, Doctor Jesus,
please come quick.
My tummy's aching and I feel sick.
I know prayer can do the trick;
thank you, Doctor Jesus.'

Well, if you're feeling kinda funny
and your nose is very runny,
your chicken pox are scratchy
and your face is red and patchy.
Your mumps are big and bumpy
and you're feeling kinda grumpy
here's what you should do.

Say 'Doctor, Doctor Jesus,
please come quick.
My tummy's aching and I feel sick.
I know prayer can do the trick;
thank you, Doctor Jesus.' *(x3)*

432 James Wright

Christmas bells that bring glad tidings,
carols full of joy and cheer.
Fairy lights that shine and glisten,
how I love this time of year.
But within my heart I cherish,
more than all my eyes can see,
one small child laid in a manger,
heaven's gift of love to me.

> *What a wondrous gift from heaven,*
> *heaven's gift of love to me.*
> *One small baby in a manger,*
> *heaven's gift of love to me.*

Christmas carols and decorations,
choc'lates on the Christmas tree.
Giving gifts to one another,
meeting friends and family.
But within my heart I cherish,
more than all my eyes can see,
one small child laid in a manger,
heaven's gift of love to me.

433 Sue McClellan, John Paculabo and Keith Ryecroft

Colours of day dawn into the mind,
the sun has come up, the night is
    behind.
Go down in the city, into the street,
and let's give the message to the people
    we meet.

> *So light up the fire and let the flame*
>   *burn,*
> *open the door, let Jesus return.*
> *Take seeds of his Spirit, let the fruit*
>   *grow,*
> *tell the people of Jesus, let his love*
>   *show.*

Go through the park, on into the town;
the sun still shines on; it never goes
    down.
The light of the world is risen again;
the people of darkness are needing a
    friend.

Open your eyes, look into the sky,
the darkness has come, the sun came to
    die.
The evening draws on, the sun
    disappears,
but Jesus is living, his Spirit is near.

434 Paul Field

Come and join in the party
on the kingdom's shore.
Come and join in the party,
there's always room for more.
Ev'rybody's invited
to find the love that's true.
So come and join in the party,
Jesus welcomes you.

One day while they were fishing
some of Jesus' friends
saw him walking upon the shore,
heard him call to them:

When you're sailing a stormy sea,
you don't know what to do:
look for Jesus upon the shore,
hear him call to you.

435 Pete Norman

Come let's bow down and worship him,
let's kneel before the Lord.
For he is our God, who made us,
we are the people under his care.
And we cry, 'Holy, holy, holy is the Lord.'

436 Brian Doerksen

Come, now is the time to worship.
Come, now is the time to give your
    heart.
Come, just as you are to worship.
Come, just as you are before your God,
    come.

One day ev'ry tongue will confess you
    are God,
one day ev'ry knee will bow.
Still, the greatest treasure remains for
    those
who gladly choose you now.

437 David MacGregor

Come on and shine, shine, shine
(oh, we can shine), shine out for Jesus.
Love, love, love
(oh, we can love) the way he did.
Live, live, live
(oh, we can live), live like him always.
Shine out for Jesus,
live and love like him.

438 John Hardwick

Come on, let's celebrate
because our God is great.
He is worthy of our praise.
Come on, let's celebrate
because our God is great,
so let's shout out his name.
Give me a 'J',
give me an 'E',
give me an 'S',
give me a 'U',
give an 'S'.
Who is great?
J E S U S.
That's who it is, Jesus.
(Repeat)

439 Bev Gammon

Come on, let's go exploring,
let's find the truth in the Bible,
digging into God's word.

Is it only for grown ups? *No! No! No!*
Is it all very boring? *No!*
Is it all just made up? *No! No! No!*
Is it just fairy stories? *No!*

Is it all about Jesus? *Yes! Yes! Yes!*
He's our friend Jesus. *Yes!*
Jesus who loves us. *Yes! Yes! Yes!*
Jesus who saves us. *Yes!*

He's there when you're lonely. *Praise the Lord!*
He's there when you're happy. *Praise him!*
He's there in the night-time. *Praise the Lord!*
He's there in the daytime. *Praise him!*

440 Mark G. Rowe

Come on, let's raise our voice,
let's make an awesome noise
because God is in our land.
Come on, let's tell the world
in case they haven't heard
through Jesus we can stand.

Come on, let's dance and shout
because the truth is out,
that God is in our land.
Come on, let's serve our King,
let's keep on listening;
we wait for his command.

Before the throne of God,
because he shed his blood
he's joined our hearts together
by the pow'r of his love.
A multi-coloured people,
one nation under heaven above.
A multi-coloured people,
one nation under heaven above.

(Repeat verses 1 and 2)

For our sin is erased from his memory,
downloaded grace and favour to
*   humanity.*
A multi-coloured people,
one nation under heaven above.
A multi-coloured people,
one nation under heaven above.

Jesus Christ is Lord. *(x7)*
Christ is Lord and King over every land. *(x3)*

441 Andrew & Wendy Rayner

Countdown for the King.
Countdown for the King.
The time has come for ev'ryone,
for all the world to sing.
Countdown for the King.
Countdown for the King.
Ev'ryone across the world
lift your voice and sing.

Two thousand years ago
God came to earth as man,
bringing a hope for life
and all that is to come.

Now we commemorate
a pinnacle of time,
then we will celebrate
when Christ returns again.

No more death or mourning,
no more crying or pain;
all old things will pass away.
Ev'ry eye shall see him
every knee shall bow.
Praise and honour,
glory and power for ever.

442 Godfrey Rust

Daniel knelt to say his prayers three
    times ev'ry day.
Jealous men, they passed a law, they
    said, 'Daniel, you can't pray.'
The king said, 'Daniel, listen here, I will
    not be defied.
You'll have to go in that lions' den.'
But Daniel, he replied,
'Why worry, God's in charge, the Lord of
    the land and sea.
I'm not afraid of your lions' teeth, 'cos
    he'll take care of me.'

The Lord said, 'Noah, build a boat in
    the middle of dry land.
Make it big enough to hold a zoo and
    wait for my command.'
The people, they all laughed at him, 'Old
    Noah's lost his head,
he's building boats for pigs and goats!'
But Noah, he just said,
'Why worry, God's in charge, the Lord of
    the land and sea.
Wasn't that a drop of rain? Well, he'll
    take care of me.'

Goliath stood there eight feet tall, what
    could the people do?
The Lord said, 'David, bring your sling,
    I've got a job for you.'
Now when he saw that little boy, Goliath,
    he went wild.
He laughed till he was fit to burst, but
    David, he just smiled (and said)
'Why worry, God's in charge, the Lord of
    the land and sea.
I'll only need one little stone, 'cos he'll
    take care of me.'

Well, Daniel found the lions tame and
    Noah, he stayed dry.
Goliath crashed down to the ground,
    you know the reason why.
And God says 'Listen, I don't change, I'm
    still the same today.
No matter what you have to face, I want
    to hear you say:
'Why worry, God's in charge, the Lord of
    the land and sea.
I put my trust in the one who saves, and
    he'll take care of me.''

443 Fred Chedgey

Daniel, *(clap, clap)* Shadrach, *(clap, clap,
clap)* Meshach, Abednego. *(x2)*
The king said, 'Worship only me or die
    for your unbelief.'
But the people saw God save all four
    from the fire and the lion's teeth.
Daniel, *(clap, clap)* Shadrach, *(clap, clap,
clap)* Meshach, Abednego.
They trusted in their Father God and
    wanted all the world to know.

444 John Hardwick

Declare it in the north,
declare it in the south,
Jesus Christ is Lord.
Declare it in the east,
declare it in the west,
Jesus Christ is Lord.
He's the Man of the Millennium;
from generation to generation.
Let's declare it across the nation!
Jesus Christ is Lord.
Jesus Christ is Lord.
He never wrote a book or song
or appeared on TV,
yet millions choose to follow him;
millions are now free.

445 Leanne Mitchell

Don't hide your light,
but shine out bright,
don't worry what to wear,
for like the birds of the air
God will take care of you,
he will look after you:
do not worry about a thing.

'Cos we're living in a topsy, turvy
kingdom,
an inside out, upside down, topsy,
turvy kingdom.
Where the words of Jesus turn
all things the other way around.

Remember to pray every day
for those you don't like, do not put up a
fight.
Give out lots of love like your Father
above
and you'll make a difference too.

Give to the poor, it says in God's law,
be like the wise man who didn't build on
the sand:
he built on the rock, so he wasn't
knocked
when the rain came pouring down.

446 Chris Jackson

Don't worry (don't worry),
don't worry (don't worry),
don't worry about a thing.
(Repeat)

But in all your prayers
ask God for what you need,
always asking him with a thankful heart.

447 Andy Read

Doo doo doo doo doo doo doo. (x4)

I need you in the morning and I need
you at night.
I need you in the darkness when having
a fright.
I hate mashed potato, but the beans are
OK.
I can choose right from wrong, please
show me the way.

I need you, you, you, I need you.

I need you in my heart and I need you in
my mind.
I need you just to help me to be loving
and kind.
I hate fried rice but the chips are OK.
I can choose right from wrong, please
show me the way.

I need you inside for the rest of my life.
I need to take time just to follow the
    light.
I love a bit of bread and I love a bit of
    wine.
Nothing like communion just to keep me
    in line.

448 Bev Gammon

Do what you know is right (do what you
    know is right).
Do what you know is good (do what is
    good).

All
If no one else does it, don't be afraid.
Jesus says, 'I am with you always.'

449 John Lane

Do you dash or do you dawdle?
Do you rush or do you roam?
Do you leap or do you waddle?
Do you creep or do you stride?

There are choices to be making;
what direction will we take?
Making moves to follow Jesus,
not just wandering, oh no!

Why don't you
take a little step closer to Jesus? (x3)
Never let anything keep you away.

One day kids ran up to Jesus,
hoping he would bless them all;
adults sniffed and snarled and snorted:
'He's got no time for you at all!'
Jesus' face was sad and frowning,
'Don't you dare push kids around!
They're most welcome in God's kingdom;
I'm sure glad to have them round.'

Just keep on
taking little steps closer to Jesus. (x3)
Never let anyone keep you away!

450 Michael Forster

Do you ever wish you could fly like a
    bird,
or burrow like a worm? Well, how
    absurd!
Think of all the things that you can do
and just be glad God made you 'you'!

Do you ever wish you could swim like a
    duck?
Unless your feet are webbed you're out
    of luck!
Think of all the things that you can do
and just be glad God made you 'you'!

Do you ever wish you could run like a
    hare?
Well, wishing it won't get you anywhere!
Think of all the things that you can do
and just be glad God made you 'you'!

Do you ever wish you could hang like a
    bat?
There's really not a lot of fun in that!
Think of all the things that you can do
and just be glad God made you 'you'!

Continued overleaf

Do you ever wish – well, that's really
   enough!
To wish away your life is silly stuff!
Think of all the things that you can do
and just be glad God made you 'you'!

451   Graham Kendrick

*Ev'rybody ev'rywhere, bless his holy
   name.*
Ev'rybody ev'rywhere, for ever.
*Ev'rybody ev'rywhere, sing about his
   love.*
*Ev'rybody ev'rywhere, for ever and
   ever.*

I will praise you my God and King
and bless your name each day and for
   ever.
Great is the Lord, greatly praise him.
His greatness knows no boundaries.
Oh, let each generation stand in awe
and tell their children what he's done.
I will meditate upon your glory,
splendour and majesty, mighty miracles.
Let them be on ev'ry tongue,
tell the glorious things you've done.

God is kind and merciful,
he is slow to anger, always rich in love,
all that he does full of compassion.
Creatures and creation give you thanks,
your people bless your holy name
telling the glories of your reign.
They will tell the world about your glory,
splendour and majesty, mighty miracles,
and this glorious King shall reign
generations without end.

See him lift the fallen,
share the burden as we walk the weary
   road.
The eyes of all look up to heaven
for he is our helper, our provider
and the source that satisfies
the needs of ev'ry living thing.
The Lord is always fair and full of
   kindness,
close to all who call, seek him truly.
He fulfils their hearts' desire
but the wicked he destroys.

452   James Wright

Ev'rybody is special to God,
ev'rybody is important to God,
and when you think that you don't
   matter a lot,
don't forget that you're a child of the
   King.
Ev'rybody is special to God,
ev'rybody is important to God,
and when you think that you don't
   matter a lot,
don't forget that you're a child of the
   King.
For he has called us, ev'ry one,
to be his chosen daughters and sons.
And he has blessed us each one the
   same
with unconditional love.

Rap:
Now you may be big, or you may be
   small,
now you may be rich, or you may be
   poor,
now you may be wide, or you may be
   thin,
but don't forget whatever shape you're
   in, that . . .

453 Mark & Helen Johnson

Ev'ry Christmas we remember
baby Jesus, born to the world.
For this reason each December is a
  special
time for us all.

Ev'ry Christmas we partake in
fruit and biscuits, pudding and pies.
But when all the food is eaten
lies a message true for all time.

  So sing a song, ev'ryone celebrate,
  the time has come, this is a special
  date!

Ev'ry Christmas we're all busy
buying gifts and seasonal cards.
But behind this old tradition
lies a present come from the past.

Ev'ry Christmas we have pleasure
seeing all the glitter and lights.
But there is a brighter treasure
to be found in Jesus Christ.

  So sing a song, ev'ryone celebrate,
  the time has come, this is a special
  date!

Ev'ry Christmas there are parties
fun and laughter, music and games.
But the best place we can start is
finding Jesus once again.

Ev'ry Christmas we remember
baby Jesus born to the world.
For this reason each December
is a special time for us all!

454 Dave Cooke and Paul Field

  Ev'ry day let me be trusting you
  for all I need.
  Ev'ry night I will pray:
  thank you for loving me ev'ry day.

Lord, you know there are times
when my faith is hard to find.
Even then you let me know
your love won't let me go.

Through my joy, in my tears,
you will be throughout the years,
a faithful God whose word is true:
teach me to live in you.

455 Doug Horley

  Faith as small as a mustard seed
  will move mountains, move mountains.
  Faith as small as a mustard seed
  will move mountains by the power of
  God.
  (Repeat)

Believe what Jesus said was true,
believe he meant it just for you.
Wait and see what God will do,
as you pray, pray, as you pray.

  Faith as small as a mustard seed
  will move mountains, move mountains.
  Faith as small as a mustard seed
  will move mountains by the power of
  God.

Do da do da do da do do da,
do da do da mountains.
Do da do da do da do do da,
do da do da mustard.

456 Paul Crouch and David Mudie

Father, I'm willing to hear what you say,
give me, oh give me a message each
    day.
I just want to hear you, whatever I do;
please speak to me plainly in words
    clear and true.

Father, forgive me when I don't want to
    hear,
draw me, oh draw me until I am near.
I want you to use me however you can,
oh take me and use me and all that I am.

Father, you've given a book sent from
    you,
Father, oh Father, with words clear and
    true.
Oh help me to read it as much as I can,
and then you can use me and all that I
    am.

457 Jenny Hewer

Father, I place into your hands
the things I cannot do.
Father, I place into your hands
the things that I've been through.
Father, I place into your hands
the way that I should go,
for I know I always can trust you.

Father, I place into your hands
my friends and family.
Father, I place into your hands
the things that trouble me.
Father, I place into your hands
the person I would be,
for I know I always can trust you.

Father, we love to see your face,
we love to hear your voice,
Father, we love to sing your praise
and in your name rejoice,
Father, we love to walk with you
and in your presence rest,
for we know we always can trust you.

Father, I want to be with you
and do the things you do.
Father, I want to speak the words
that you are speaking too.
Father, I want to love the ones
that you will draw to you,
for I know that I am one with you.

458 Alison Moon

Father, I praise you,
you mean ev'rything to me.
Help me to live close to you ev'ry day,
may I keep on praising you.

Jesus, I serve you,
you're my Saviour and my friend.
Help me to live close to you ev'ry day,
may I keep on serving you.

Spirit, I love you,
you're there when I feel alone.
Help me to live close to you ev'ry day,
may I keep on loving you.

459 Kate Abba

Father, we give you ourselves today,
    amen. *(x3)*

Jesus, we give you ourselves today,
    amen. *(x3)*

Spirit, we give you ourselves today,
amen. *(x3)*

Amen. *(x6)*

460 Unknown

Fisherman Peter on the sea,
drop your net, boy, and follow me! *(x2)*

Rich young ruler, plain to see,
can't love money and follow me! *(x2)*

Lonely Zacchaeus in the tree,
love your neighbour and follow me! *(x2)*

Nicodemus, Pharisee,
new life comes when you follow me! *(x2)*

Doubting Thomas, from doubt be free,
stop your doubting and follow me! *(x2)*

461 Mike Burn

Fly free, Spirit of God,
fly free, free as a dove,
draw me up in your flights of love.
Show me all that you see,
help me to feel what you feel,
reveal the Father's heart for this land.

The Spirit of God is brooding
over this land.
The Spirit of God is singing
of the Father's plans.
The Spirit of God is waiting;
longing for the day
when the praises of God will ring
loud and clear once more.

The church of God is stirring
all through this land.
The church of God is praying,
lifting holy hands.
The church of God is rising,
rising to take her place,
joining heavenly hosts
singing praises to the Lamb.

462 Colin Buchanan based on 2 Timothy 1:7

Oh! Wo oh! Wo oh! *(x2)*

For God *(for God)* did not *(did not)*
give us a spirit of timidity,
but a *(but a)* spirit *(spirit)*
of power *(of power)*
of love and of self-discipline.

2 Timothy, chapter one, verse seven
(2 Timothy, chapter one, verse seven).
(Repeat)

Oh! Wo oh! Wo oh! *(x2)*

463 Steve and Kay Morgan-Gurr

For God so loved the world,
he gave his one and only Son,
that all who trust him and believe,
have life forever on.
And if I were the only one
who let him down and turned away,
he'd still love me as his own,
and just for me he'd pay.

464 John L. Hardwick

For God so loved the world
he gave his only Son,
and whoever believes in him
shall not die, but have eternal life.

L is for the love that he has for me,
I am the reason he died on the tree,
F is for forgiveness and now I am free,
E is to enjoy being in his company.

465 Paul Crouch and David Mudie

For the foolishness of God
is wiser than man's wisdom,
and the weakness of God
is stronger than man's strength.
(Repeat)

God knows all about the world,
the things that we can't see,
the things that we don't understand,
that baffle you and me.
His strength is never-ending
and we are weak and small.
His hand supports the universe
and he is in control.

For the foolishness of God
is wiser than man's wisdom,
and the weakness of God
is stronger than man's strength.
(Repeat)

466 Doug and Jamie Horley

For the measure of the treasure
that you store in heaven,
is the measure that'll last forever.
But the measure of the treasure
that you store on earth
might be carried away by a thief one
     day,
or rot when the moths get hungry.
(Repeat)

For where your treasure is,
that's where your heart is.
For where your treasure is
there'll be your heart.
(Repeat)

467 Matt Redman

Friend of sinners, Lord of truth,
I am falling in love with you.
Friend of sinners, Lord of truth,
I have fallen in love with you.
Jesus, I love your name,
the name by which we're saved.
Jesus, I love your name,
the name by which we're saved.

Friend of sinners, Lord of truth,
I am giving my life to you.
Friend of sinners, Lord of truth,
I have given my life to you.
Jesus, I love your name,
the name by which we're saved.
Jesus, I love your name,
the name by which we're saved.

468 James Wright

From the top of my head to the tips of
    my toes,
I am fearfully and wonderf'lly made,
from the colour of my eyes to the shape
    of my nose,
I am fearfully and wonderf'lly made.
Created in the image of God,
created to give him praise,
from the top of my head to the tips of
    my toes,
I am fearfully and wonderf'lly made.

From the way that I hear to the way that
    I talk,
I am fearfully and wonderf'lly made,
from the way that I see to the way that I
    walk,
I am fearfully and wonderf'lly made.
Created in the image of God,
created to give him praise,
from the way that I hear to the way that
    I talk,
I am fearfully and wonderf'lly made.

469 Steve Burnhope

Genesis, Exodus, Leviticus,
Numbers, Deuteronomy, Joshua, Judges,
Ruth and one and two Samuel,
one and two Kings and one and two
    Chronicles,
Ezra, Nehemiah.

Esther, Job and Psalms and Proverbs,
Ecclesiastes, Song of Solomon,
Isaiah, Jeremiah, Lamentations,
Ezekiel, Daniel, and Hosea and Joel.

Amos, Obadiah, Jonah, Micah,
Nahum, Habbakuk, Zephaniah,
Haggai, Zechariah, Malachi,
that's it, thirty-nine books in all.

470 Mike Burn

Give and it shall be given!
Oh, you can't out-give the Lord your
    God.
One thing is certain in the kingdom of
    heaven,
the measure you give is the measure
    you'll receive.

    And it'll be pressed down, shaken
        together and overflowing,
    it'll be pressed down, shaken together
        and overflowing.

Don't rob God of your firstfruits,
give the most you can and then some
    more.
He longs to open a window from heaven
and pour out a blessing so big you'll be
    amazed!

God's building now his kingdom
and his kingdom's rule will never end.
If you will give him your life, your time,
    your money,
you'll store up a treasure no one can
    steal away.

471 Kate Abba

Give thanks to the Lord for he is good,
hallelujah,
for God's love has no end,
hallelujah.
Let all you people here,
hallelujah,
sing and shout for joy,
shout for joy.

Give thanks to the Lord for he is good,
hallelujah,
God's right hand raised me up,
hallelujah.
Let me sing and sing again,
hallelujah,
sing and shout for joy,
shout for joy.

There's so many songs I want to sing,
Lord, I love you, and the joy you bring.
Morning breaks another day,
and you chase the clouds away,
Lord, I really want to say,
you're the good who shines my way.

Give thanks to the Lord for he is good,
hallelujah,
I am weak but you are strong,
hallelujah.
You are God and I exalt,
hallelujah,
sing and shout for joy,
shout for joy.

There's so many songs I want to sing,
Lord, I love you, and the joy you bring.
Morning breaks another day,
and you chase the clouds away,
Lord, I really want to say,
you're the good who shines my way.

Give thanks to the Lord for he is good,
hallelujah,
his right hand has raised me up,
hallelujah.
Let me sing and sing again,
hallelujah,
sing and shout for joy,
shout for joy.
Sing and shout for joy,
shout for joy.
Sing and shout for joy,
shout for joy.

472 Nick Harding

God can give a very special life.
That's the life I see,
and I know that if I will say 'yes'
God's got a plan for me.

God can give a very special life.
That's the greatest way,
and I know that if I will say 'yes'
I'll live for God each day.

473 Susanna Levell

God created the world and all he had
    made,
he saw it was good.
God is worthy of praise, for all he has
    made,
it is very good.
In the beginning he made heavens
    and earth,
now never ending I will tell of his
    worth.
God created the world and all he had
    made,
he saw it was good.

On the first day God said, 'Let there be
    light'
so parting light and darkness, he called
    it day and night.
On the second day God said, 'Let there
    be space'
so separating waters put the land, sea
    and sky in place.

On the third day God said, 'Let there be
    growth',
the land produced plantation, the trees
    and flow'rs did grow.
On the fourth day God said, 'Let there
    be lights'.
The sun to govern the daytime and the
    moon and stars for night.

On the fifth day God said, 'Let there be
    life'.
He filled the sea with creatures, and
    birds, they filled the sky.
On the sixth day God said, 'Let there be
    man'.
First animals he made, then in his image
    he made man.

By the seventh day all the work of his
    hands
was finished to completion, his perfect
    mighty plan.
On this special day God said, 'Let it be
    blessed'.
So he rested, made it holy as a special
    day of rest.

474   Amanda Lofts

God gave me fingers that I can wiggle,
I tickle my friends and make them
    giggle.
Fingers are such useful things.
Thank you, God, for fingers.

God gave me eyes so I can see
the lovely world that's all around me.
Flowers and trees of ev'ry size.
Thank you, God, for my eyes.

God gave me ears so I can hear
beautiful music loud and clear.
People talking far and near.
Thank you, God, for my ears.

God gave me a mouth so I can chew
and happily eat up all of my food.
I sing and laugh and talk and shout.
Thank you, God, for my mouth.

God gave me feet so I can run.
I can hop, skip and jump and have such
    fun.
I even walk slowly down the street.
Thank you, God, for my feet.

475   Andy Read

God has been good to me,
God has been good to me,
God has been good to me
and I will live for him. *(x2)*

Through the day and night,
through the wrong and right,
he remembers me;
how could I forget the truth that . . .

476   Alison Moon

God has put his angels to watch over me.
God has put his angels to protect me
    from all harm.
God has put his angels to see that I
    don't fall.
What a loving God, who cares so much
    for me.

477 Andy Read

God is good, he is great.
I will serve him all my days. *(x4)*

For he is faithful, wise and true;
worthy of our worship,
ruler over all,
holy and perfect.
(Yes, God is good!)

For he mighty, strong to save,
gen'rous, full of kindness,
God above all gods,
powerful in mercy.
(Yes, God is good!)

478 Jennie Flack

God is so wonderful, God is so clever.
Look at the way that God's put me
    together:
ears that can hear and eyes that can
    see.
Oh, what a wonderful, wonderful me!

*I can run with my feet,
I can clap with my hands, I can hug,
I can smile, I can sing.
With my mind I have learned
that without God, my Maker,
I wouldn't have all of these things.*

God is so wonderful, God is so clever.
Look at the way that God's put me
    together:
a mind to think up things and dream
    lovely dreams.
Oh, what a wonderful life it all means!

479 Nick Harding

*God knows me, God knows me,
God knows me better than I know
    myself.*
(Repeat)

He knows the hair on my head,
the colour of my eyes,
the thoughts in my mind,
and things down deep inside.

He knows me good and bad,
happy and sad,
frown or smile,
he knows me all the while.

480 Paul Harvey based on John 3:16

God loved the world so much (so much!)
that he gave his only Son (his Son!)
so that ev'ryone who believes in him
would have eternal life (have life!).
(Repeat)

481 Andrew and Pauline Pearson

God loves me and ev'rything about me,
God loves me and all my family.
God loves me and ev'rything about me,
God loves me and all my family.

God loves you and ev'rything about you,
God loves you and all your family. *(x2)*

God knows me and ev'rything about me,
God knows me and all my family. *(x2)*

God knows you and ev'rything about you,
God knows you and all your family. *(x2)*

482 Doug Horley

God loves me, woopah, wahey!
God loves you, woopah, wahey!
God loves us, whoopah, wahey!
God loves you.
(Repeat)

I'm gonna shout, gonna make some noise,
I'm gonna sing, gonna raise my voice,
I'm gonna dance, gonna go a little crazy,
    will you?
Will you go, will you go?

I'm gonna jump, gonna jump up high,
I'm gonna raise my hands to the sky,
I'm gonna dance, gonna go completely
    loopy, will you?

(Repeat all above)

Whoo, whoopah, wayeh-hey-eh! *(x3)*
God loves you and nothing you can do
will ever change that.
(Repeat)

God loves me, whoopah, wahey!
God loves you, whoopah, wahey!
God loves us, whoopah, wahey,
God loves you.
(Repeat)

483 Jennifer Reay

God made this world and put us here:
God made this world for us to share.
Oh what a gift for us; this planet, our
    home.
Looking around we see some ways
that we have spoiled this wonderful
    place;
God has a job for us, on this planet, our
    home.

We'll do our best for him,
oh, nothing less for him.
We're living in God's world;
what can we do to make it better?
We'll do our best for him,
oh, nothing less for him.
We've got a job to do,
it's up to me and you,
so we'll do our best for him.

So much pollution in the air,
find a solution, show we care.
Treat it with dignity; this planet, our
    home.
Forests and creatures dying out;
sadness and suff'ring, there's no doubt;
God has a job for us, on this planet, our
    home.

Do our best for God,
on this planet, our home.
It's a place to share,
on this planet, our home.
This planet, our home. *(x2)*

484 Gill Hutchinson

God of the earth and sky and sea,
great is his love for you and me.
He is the God with a loving heart.

He is the God whose word is true,
he knows the things we say and do.
He is the God with a loving heart.

He wants us all to trust him,
our maker and our friend.
He's always there beside us,
his love will never end.

He is the God who shows he cares,
he is the one who's always there,
he is the God with a loving heart.

Continued overleaf

He is the God whose praise we sing,
he is the Lord of ev'rything,
he is the God with a loving heart,
he is the God with a loving heart.

485 Kathleen Middleton

God, our Father, gave us life,
he keeps us in his care;
help us care for others too:
Lord, hear our prayer;
Lord, hear our prayer.

When we're frightened, hurt or tired,
there's always someone there.
Make us thankful for their love:
Lord, hear our prayer;
Lord hear our prayer.

All God's children need his love,
a love that we can share.
So, we pray for ev'ryone:
Lord, hear our prayer;
Lord, hear our prayer.

486 Chris Jackson

God says *(God says)*,
'Don't be afraid *(don't be afraid)*,
because I have saved you,
I have called you by name.'

God says *(God says)*,
'Don't be afraid *(don't be afraid)*,
because I have saved you,
and you are mine.'

487 Andy Read

God's hands, I'm in God's hands.
There's no safer place that I can be. *(x2)*

I don't need to worry,
I don't need to fear,
all I need to do is know that
God is near.
I don't need to tremble,
I don't need to cry,
all I need to do is know that,
God is near, God is near, God is near.

488 Andy Read

*Gonna lift you up when I'm feeling
    down.
Gonna lift you up when I'm feeling
    down, down down.
Gonna lift you up when I'm feeling
    down.
That's the place I want to be,
Holy Spirit, set me free.*
(Repeat)

Jesus is the name above ev'ry name.
Jesus is the one who will never change.
His love is faithful, true to the very end,
there is no one else who can promise
    the same!

Jesus has the pow'r over ev'ry fear,
deepest kind of love that will come so
    near.
It's knocking at the door of your very
    heart,
there is no one else who can love you
    quite the same.

489 Andy Read

Gonna live for him, gonna live for him,
gonna live for him for the rest of my life.
(x2)

I don't care what I feel,
I don't care what I see,
I'm gonna shout it out aloud:
he saved me!
Gonna live for him, gonna live for him,
gonna live for him for the rest of my
life.

Gonna follow him, gonna follow him,
gonna follow him for the rest of my life.

Gonna praise his name, gonna praise his
name,
gonna praise his name, for the rest of
my life.

© 2002 Kevin Mayhew Ltd.

490 Andy Pickford

Goodbye, goodbye to ev'ryone,
goodbye, goodbye, goodbye.
We thank you, Lord, for ev'ryone,
goodbye, we'll see you soon.
(Repeat)

The time has come for us to go,
we thank you, Lord, for being here,
to praise your name, to learn of you,
to be with friends and close to you.

This is our prayer as we go home:
please keep us safe in all we do,
please be with us at home and school;
we thank you, Lord, for loving us.

© 1999 Daybreak Music Ltd.

491 Phil Chapman

Good news of great joy
to all men on earth.
In the old town of Bethlehem,
our Saviour had his birth.

God's message to all sinful men
the same as to the shepherds then
is in these joyful words,
'A Saviour born in David's town'
and at whose name we'll all bow down,
for he is Christ the Lord!

© 2002 Kevin Mayhew Ltd.

492 James Wright

Hallelu, hallelu, hallelujah,
praise ye the Lord.
Hallelu, hallelu, come and join us
singing,
praise ye the Lord.

Now Jesus was born of Mary
in Bethlehem,
in a dusty stable with a lowly cradle
in Bethlehem.
And all the animals standing in the
straw
must have wondered who he was,
was he just the son of a carpenter,
or was this the Son of God?

Now shepherds were sat on the hillside
in Bethlehem,
when a host of angels started singing
praises
in Bethlehem.
And the night lit up with an awesome
sight
and the shepherds looked amazed,
but the angel said, 'Please do not fear,
your King is born this day.'

Continued overleaf

Hallelu, hallelu, hallelujah,
praise ye the Lord.
Hallelu, hallelu, come and join us
    singing,
praise ye the Lord.

Now wise men travelled a long way,
to Bethlehem,
from the Orient to the land of Israel
to Bethlehem.
And the star shone bright in the sky that
    night
to show them where to go,
so that they may bring gifts to the King,
myrrh, frankincense and gold.

Hail, the heav'n-born Prince of Peace!
Hail, the Sun of Righteousness!
Light and life to all he brings,
ris'n with healing in his wings;
mild he lays his glory by,
born that we no more may die,
born to raise us from the earth,
born to give us second birth.

493 Charles Wesley, George Whitefield, Martin Madan and others, alt.

Hark, the herald-angels sing
glory to the new-born King;
peace on earth and mercy mild,
God and sinners reconciled:
joyful, all ye nations rise,
join the triumph of the skies,
with th' angelic host proclaim,
'Christ is born in Bethlehem.'

Hark, the herald-angels sing
glory to the new-born King.

Christ, by highest heav'n adored,
Christ, the everlasting Lord,
late in time behold him come,
offspring of a virgin's womb!
Veiled in flesh the Godhead see,
hail th' incarnate Deity!
Pleased as man with us to dwell,
Jesus, our Emmanuel.

494 Dave Cooke

Have you ever had five thousand people
    to lunch,
then found that you've nothing in the
    fridge to munch?
It's very inconvenient and it's hard to
    ignore,
when they're climbing through the
    window and banging on the door!
But Jesus was teaching one fine day
and people came to hear what he had to
    say:
'Love your neighbour, feed the poor,
pray to God, that's what your knees are
    for!'

With God, anything is possible,
with God, anything at all.
When things appear impossible,
and pretty unbelievable,
totally improbable and very
    unpredictable,
remember, with God anything is
    possible,
with God anything at all.

And he taught for hours and it got quite
late,
the disciples checked their watches, it
was half past eight,
and they said to the crowd: 'Go and get
some food.'
But Jesus said: 'You feed this multitude.'
They said: 'We've only got five bread
rolls
and two little fishes in a very small bowl.
That's not enough for such a crowd.'
When Jesus stood up and said out loud:
'Give them to me, give them to me,
I'm gonna say grace and then you'll see.'
And he broke the bread before their
eyes,
then the food just started to multiply.

And after they had finished they could
eat no more,
there were lots of broken pieces all over
the floor,
twelve bags were collected, that's no lie,
when Jesus fed five thousand with a fish
and bread pie.

495 Graham Kendrick

Hear the sound of people singing,
all the bells are ringing
for the Christmas Child.
In the streets the lights are glowing,
but there is no knowing
of the Christmas child.

*Oh, let this Child be born in your
heart,
oh, let this Child be born in your
heart, tonight.*

Will our wars go on for ever,
and will peace be never
at Christmastime?
If we keep him in the manger
then there is no danger
from the Christmas Child.

496 Graham Kendrick

Heaven invites you to a party,
to celebrate the birth of a Son;
angels rejoicing in the starlight,
singing, 'Christ your Saviour has come.'
(Repeat)

And it's for you (and it's for you)
and it's for me (and it's for me),
for all your friends (for all your friends)
and family (and family).

Now heaven's door (now heaven's door)
is open wide (is open wide),
so come on in (so come on in),
step inside (come step inside).

Angels from the realms of glory,
wing your flight o'er all the earth;
you who sang creation's story,
now proclaim Messiah's birth.

And it's for you . . .

Let trumpets blast (let trumpets blast),
let music play (let music play),
let people shout (let people shout),
let banners wave (let banners wave).

Come, all you people (come, all you
people),
join hands together (join hands together),
bring all your neighbours
(bring all your neighbours),
everybody! (everybody!)

Continued overleaf

Send invitations (send invitations)
to every nation (to every nation),
come and adore him (come and adore
  him),
everybody! (everybody!)
everybody! (everybody!)

Heaven invites you to a party,
to celebrate the birth of a Son;
angels rejoicing in the starlight,
singing, 'Christ your Saviour has come.'

And it's for you . . .

Let trumpets blast (let trumpets blast),
let music play (let music play),
let people shout (let people shout),
let banners wave (let banners wave).

© 1988 Make Way Music

497   Margaret Carpenter

He came in love to bring hope to the
  world,
a world that had lost its way;
left heaven's home, came to earth a
  baby King
so now, ev'ry Christmas we can gladly
  sing;

Let the bells ring out,
let the people shout
songs of joy to the King,
the King of kings.
Let the bells ring out,
let the people shout
songs of joy to the King, the King of
  kings.

Let's be the first to share his love on
  earth,
for it's Christmas time again.
It is Christmas, it's that time again!

© 1999 Out of the Ark Music

498   James Wright

He can do the impossible,
change the unchangeable,
love the unlovable.
He can cleanse the uncleansable,
do the impossible in you and me.
Ev'ry storm can be stilled,
any door can be opened,
ev'ry mountain we face can be moved.
Ev'ry hurt can be healed,
any chain can be broken,
in all of these things we can prove:

© 2001 Kingsway's Thankyou Music

499   Steve and Kay Morgan-Gurr

He changed water into wine,
healed the sick and cured the blind;
told his friends where they would find
the best fish in the sea.
Miracles his power show,
though it happened long ago:
the greatest miracle I know
is what he's done for me,
what he's done for me.

Miracles are there to show
us all who Jesus was,
and to make us listen to what he said.
And they make it clear
that he's the Son of God
because no one else could give life to
  the dead.

If we turn to Jesus and
are sorry for our sin,
God's word makes it plain for all to see:
from that brand new start,
the greatest miracle begins,
the miracle of life eternally.

© 1999 Daybreak Music Ltd.

500   Andrew and Pauline Pearson

He gave me two ears to hear,
and one mouth to shout,
but unless I take time to listen to God,
I won't know what I'm shouting about.
So I'm listening to what the Father says,
I'm listening to him:
only then will I hear of his love so clear,
when I'm listening to him.

501   Andy Read

He is here, he is here,
he is here in my heart
and I will not be afraid.
(Repeat x3)

He will teach me what's right,
he will hold me at night,
he is always the closest to me.
He will show me what's wrong,
and will sing me this song,
and I will not be afraid.

502   Brian Howard

He is K I N G.
He is Lord and he is King.
He is K I N G.
Lord of lords and King of kings.
He is K I N G
of my heart, my mind,
yes, all of me.
He is K I N G,
he is my Lord, he is my King.

He is Lord and he is King
over what has been and
what will be.
Mountain tops and dark valleys,
highest heavens and the deepest seas.
K I N G, K I N . . .

He is . . .

Ev'ry other lord and king
will one day bend their knee.
In the day of his coming
they will confess, he is the King of kings!
K I N G, K I N G, K I N G: Jesus!

503   Andrew and Pauline Pearson

He is the one that sets my hands
a-clapping,
he is the one that sets my hands free.
He is the one that sets my hands
a-clapping,
he is the one for me.

I wanna tell you
I'm clapping, I'm clapping,
I'm clapping, I'm clapping,
I'm clapping, I'm clapping,
I'm clapping for my Lord.

He is the one that sets my feet
a-dancing,
he is the one that sets my feet free:
he is the one that sets my feet
a-dancing,
he is the one for me.

He is the one that sets my voice
a-singing,
he is the one that sets my voice free:
he is the one that sets my voice
a-singing,
he is the one for me.

He is the one that causes me to praise
him,
he is the one that sets me free:
he is the one that causes me to praise
him,
he is the one for me.

Continued overleaf

Last chorus:
I wanna tell you
I'm clapping, I'm dancing,
I'm singing, I'm praising,
I'm clapping, I'm dancing,
I'm singing for my Lord.

504 Andy Pickford

Hello, welcome, in the name of the Lord,
(I said), hello, welcome,
we're here to praise the Lord.
(Repeat)

We really missed you, what's been
    happening?
Good to see you, we really care:
we have a Father who's gonna bless us
    all.
Now we're here to praise his name,
now we're here to praise his name.

Hello, welcome, in the name of the Lord,
(I said), hello, welcome,
we're here to praise, we're here to
    praise,
we're here to praise the Lord.

505 Paul Harvey

He made the eyes of the blind man see,
the ears of the deaf man hear;
he made the mute tongue shout for joy,
the lame to leap like a deer.

He made the wind and the waves obey,
he kept the hungry crowd fed;
and when they laid him in the tomb,
he rose again from the dead!

His name is Jesus, he's the Saviour of
    the world,
he's right here: listen, he's talking to
    you.
His name is Jesus, he's the bright
    morning star,
he will rise in your heart and make you
    new.

506 Andy Read

He made the stars, he made the trees,
he made my mum and he made me.
He made the sun, he made the birds,
he made my smile and he made me.

Yes, the God of the earth, and the maker
    of the sea,
he's the Father of us all,
he's the God of family.
(Repeat)

507 John Hardwick

He's a rock!
His works are perfect,
all his ways are just.
He's a rock!
His works are perfect,
all his ways are just.
He's a faithful God who does no wrong;
upright and just is he!
Look up chapter thirty-two, verse four of
    Deuteronomy.
Look up chapter thirty-two, verse four of
    Deuteronomy.
Cha, cha, cha!

508 Traditional

He's got the whole world in his hand.
 (x4)

He's got you and me, brother, in his
 hand. *(x3)*
He's got the whole world in his hand.

He's got you and me, sister, in his hand.
 (x3)
He's got the whole world in his hand.

He's got the little tiny baby in his hand.
 (x3)
He's got the whole world in his hand.

He's got ev'rybody here in his hand. *(x3)*
He's got the whole world in his hand.

509 Nick Harding

He's the man who calmed the sea,
he's the man who died for me,
he turned death to victory
and everybody can meet him.

Jesus came to heal the sick,
the blind, the lost, the lame.
Jesus sends his Spirit now
to help us just the same.

Jesus, only Son of God,
who came to show the way.
Jesus walks along with us
to guide us ev'ry day.

There's a message for the world,
good news for us to share.
We can make a diff'rence now
but only if we dare!

510 Ron Sivers

Hey! Hey! celebrate!
Jesus is our Saviour.
Hey! Hey! celebrate!
Jesus is our King.
Things will never be the same,
our lives have been completely changed.
We'll give all praise to him,
we will exalt his name,
he will for ever reign.

511 Philip and Stephanie Chapman

Hey there, Mister Scarecrow,
standing out in the sun,
what are the wonders you have seen
as the seasons follow the sun?

I've seen the dark earth turn to green
as the shoots come creeping through.
I've felt the gentle rains of spring
falling from skies of blue.
I've heard the song-birds calling
as the sun lights up the day,
and I've known that God has made this
 world
in a very, very, very, very, very special way.

I've seen the tall corn waving
like the waves out on the sea.
I've felt the breeze a-blowing
and the sun that warms me.
I've heard the children's voices
as they laugh and as they play,
and I've known that God has made this
 world
in a very, very, very, very, very special way.

512 Tony Cooke

High, high, high,
high, high, high,
lift him up, lift up Jesus high!
High, high, high,
high, high, high,
lift him up, lift up Jesus high!

The name of the Lord,
the name of the Lord
is greatly to be praised!
He is my strength and he is my shield,
he's good in all his ways!

He's near to all who call on him
and bless his holy name!
He's good to you and good to me
and good in all his ways!

Hi! I'm a 'rangutan, God made me.
Hi! I'm a porpoise in the sea, God made
me.
Hi! I'm an aardvark, God made me.
Hi! I'm a panda bear, God made me.
Well, I'm a 'rangutan, and through the
trees I swing.
I am a singing, swinging 'rangutan.
I'm a porpoise, hey, with this smile on
my face!
God gave me a heart to play.
And I'm an aardvark, and if you're really
smart,
you know my name starts with two 'A's.
I'm a panda bear, black here, white
there.
How do you like the little suit I wear?

Hi! I'm a child of God, God made me.
Hi! I'm a child of God, he walks and
talks with me.
Hi! I'm a child of God, he hears me
when I pray.
Hi! I'm a child of God, and I was made in
his image.

513 Brian Howard

Hi! I'm a penguin, God made me.
Hi! I'm a kangaroo, God made me.
Hi! I'm an elephant, God made me.
Hi! I'm a baby monkey, God made me.
I'm a penguin and I walk kind of funny.
Can you walk like me?
I'm a kangaroo and I bounce around the
room.
Can you bounce like me?
I'm an elephant and I can use my trunk
to pick a coconut from the tree.
I'm a baby monkey, I can climb up and
down,
up and down that coconut tree.

514 Bev Gammon

Holy Spirit, fill me now,
I want to be like Jesus;
show me how I can live like him.

Holy Spirit, teach me now,
I want to speak for Jesus;
tell me how I can speak for him.

Holy Spirit, help me now,
I want to love like Jesus,
show me how I can love like him.

515 Suzi de Faye

Holy Spirit, Holy Spirit,
pour your pow'r, pour your pow'r
on me, on me, on me.

Holy Spirit, Holy Spirit,
send your fire, send your fire,
pour your pow'r, pour your pow'r
on me, on me, on me.

Holy Spirit, Holy Spirit,
talk to me, talk to me,
send your fire, send your fire,
pour your pow'r, pour your pow'r
on me, on me, on me.

Holy Spirit, Holy Spirit,
guide my life, guide my life,
talk to me, talk to me,
send your fire, send your fire,
pour your pow'r, pour your pow'r
on me, on me, on me.

Holy Spirit, Holy Spirit,
bring your healing, bring your healing,
guide my life, guide my life,
talk to me, talk to me,
send your fire, send your fire,
pour your pow'r, pour your pow'r
on me, on me, on me.

Holy Spirit, Holy Spirit,
set me free, set me free,
bring your healing, bring your healing,
guide my life, guide my life,
talk to me, talk to me,
send your fire, send your fire,
pour your pow'r, pour your pow'r
on me, on me, on me.

516 Nick Harding

How does sun shine in the sky?
How do clouds float by?
How do seeds grow into trees?
How do leaves sway in the breeze?

*So many things to understand,
put in place by God's hand.*

How do fish live in the sea?
How am I like me?
How can I think what to say?
How does night turn into day?

How does God teach us to grow?
How much can I know?
Why does God show love and care?
Why is Jesus always there?

517 Dave Cooke

I am H A P P Y,
I've got a reason, just ask me why.
I can S M I L E,
it's very easy, as you can see.
I can S H O U T,
it's gonna be loud, you will agree.
It's so G R E A T that I know him and he
    knows me.
(Repeat)

*And he knows my name,
loves me just the same;
and I want to say
each and ev'ry day
that he's a friend of mine,
to the end of time.
It's so good to know
that from the heavens above
to the earth below,
he loves me so.*

Continued overleaf

I can S T A N D,
say that he's so good to me.
I can W A L K,
and know he's with me ev'ry day.
I can D A N C E,
and sing my song in any key.
And I can S P E A K
and tell you that he's the only way.

And he knows my name,
loves me just the same;
and I want to say
each and ev'ry day
that he's a friend of mine,
to the end of time.
It's so good to know
that from the heavens above
to the earth below,
he loves me so.

518   Andy Read

I am loved by the Father,
the maker of creation.
I've been bought with a price so high
and nothing will take me away from his
  love.

Abba Father (Abba Father),
Abba Father (Abba Father),
Abba Father (Abba Father),
Abba Father.

I am treasured by the Father
who delights in my life.
There is no separation,
and nothing will take me away from his
  love.

I am hugged by you, Father,
I'm secure in your arms.
No harm will come to me,
and nothing will take me away from your
  love.

519   Andrew and Pauline Pearson

I am special, loved, accepted and
*   forgiven,*
I am the apple of God's eye.
I am special, loved, accepted,
special, loved, protected
and I don't even have to try.
(Repeat)

He loved me before the world began,
he calls me by my name:
his love will last for all time,
and will never, ever change, never change.

520   Pat Turner

I believe in God the Father,
I believe in God the Son.
I believe Calvary
was forgiving love for me.
I receive, I believe.

I believe in you, my Jesus,
I believe you reign above.
I believe, Three-in-One;
let your Holy Spirit come.
I receive, I believe.

I believe the resurrection,
I believe you live in me.
I believe I am known,
I am called before your throne.
I receive, I believe.

I am known, I am called before your
    throne.
I receive, I believe.

521 Iain D. Craig

I believe in J. E. S. U. S.
I believe in J. E. S. U. S.
I believe in J. E. S. U. S.
I believe in Jesus.
(Repeat)

He is Saviour and Messiah.
He is my best friend,
and it's true, he really loves me.
His love will never end.

He walked upon the water,
he made the blind see.
And fed five thousand people
by the shores of Galilee.

It was on Good Friday
they hung him on a tree,
but only three days later
he rose for you and me.

522 Philip and Stephanie Chapman

I can learn about numbers one and two,
I can measure the jump of a kangaroo.
And while I'm walking around the zoo
I can add up the spots on a leopard too.
But I want someone I can count on
whenever I'm happy or I'm blue.
Someone who'll always love me,
Jesus I can count on you.
La, la, la, la, la, la . . .

I can count on my fingers up to ten,
I can run round the field and back again.
When I'm trav'lling I count the cars
but I run out of numbers when I'm
    counting stars.
But I want someone I can count on
whenever I'm happy or I'm blue.
Someone who'll always love me,
Jesus I can count on you.
La, la, la, la, la, la . . .

523 Andrew and Pauline Pearson

I can sing, 'La, la', I can shout 'Hurray'.
I can dance around and around all day.
I can clap my hands, I can raise them
    high,
when I praise, when I praise, when I
    praise the Lord.

I can stand very still, I can jump very
    high,
I can march around and around all day,
I can close my eyes, (I can) quietly pray,
when I praise, when I praise, when I
    praise the Lord.

524 Caroline Brader

I don't know why a bird has to fly,
why doesn't it walk like me?
And I don't know how
we get milk from a cow,
when it only eats grass for it tea.
And I am not sure
what belly buttons are for,
it's a mystery to me.
The one thing I know
is Jesus loves me,
and so that's the answer for me.

Continued overleaf

Let me explain, let me tell you once
again,
as Jesus' friend you'll find his love
never ends,
and that's the answer for me.

I don't know why my Gran's apple pie
only tastes right with ice cream.
And I don't know who
discovered sunflowers grew
all from one tiny seed.
And I don't know how
we could ever allow
repeats on our TV.
The one thing I know
is Jesus loves me
and so that's the answer for me.

525   Ian Smale

If anyone is in Christ,
he is a new creation.
The old has gone
and the new has come.

526   Mark and Helen Johnson

If I go to the furthest place that I could
go,
he'll be there, he'll be there.
To the east or the west, to the sun or
snow,
he will always be there!

Oh yeah! (he'll be there) oh yeah!
(he'll be there)
he will never leave me.
I know! (oh I know) he cares,
(how he cares)
he's the only one I know who's always
there!

In the dark of the night or in the light of
day,
he'll be there, he'll be there.
When I'm all on my own, or I've lost my
way,
he will always be there!

When I'm down in the dumps and things
are looking bad,
he'll be there, he'll be there.
When I'm over the moon (when I'm really
glad),
he will always be there!

527   Phil Overton

I find my happiness, (oh yes!)
I find my happiness,
I find my happiness
in keeping your commands.

Don't make gods of earthly idols.
Don't envy others' gain.
Keep one day special for the Lord.
Don't take his name in vain.

Do not murder, do not steal.
Be faithful to your wife.
Love your mother and your father.
Do not cheat or lie.

528   Sammy Horner

If I've been wrong, and I've been bad,
if I've made my Saviour sad,
then how come I don't get what I
deserve?

If I've been wicked all my days,
if there is a price to pay,
how come I don't get what I deserve?

If the Lord above's forgiven me,
shown me mercy constantly,
then it seems to me that we
should do the same for others
    consistently.

If I've been a lying, cheating fool,
if I treat my neighbour cruel,
How come I don't get what I deserve?

529   Mike Burn

If you believe, you will receive
whatever you ask for in prayer.
If you believe, you will receive
whatever you ask for in prayer.
Matthew twenty-one, verse twenty-two.

530   Mark and Helen Johnson

If you're feeling sad and weary
and you're down in the dumps,
down in the dumps, down in the dumps,
if you're feeling sad and weary
and you're down in the dumps,
there's something you can do.

Don't be grumpy, don't go on and on,
don't be grumpy, don't you spoil the fun!

Count your blessings, name them one by
    one,
count your blessings, see what God has
    done!

531   John Fryer

If you wanna be cool and live in God's
    sight,
obeying his rules and doing what's
    right,
then don't be a fool, live in the light
and be free, free, free, free, free.

Jesus said, 'If you really love me,
then you will do the things I say.'

If you wanna be ace and live in his way,
let the King take his place – do it today!
We're under his grace but still must
    obey,
to be free, free, free, free, free.

If you wanna be brill and live life his
    way,
then tell him you will (and do what you
    say).
With his Spirit he'll fill you every day,
to be free, free, free, free, free.

532   J. D. Bullen

If you want to know why Noah built a
    boat,
why Joseph had a very special coat,
how God took dust and gave it life,
made Adam and then Eve, his wife.
Where can you find all these amazing
    things?

Look in the Bible, the Bible,
the B. I. B. L. E, the B. I. B. L. E,
look in the Bible, the Bible.
God's book he's given to you and me.

Continued overleaf

If you want to know why
Samson was long-haired,
why Daniel with the lions was not
   scared,
Jacob dreaming of a ladder,
Moses' stick turned to an adder.
Where can you find all these amazing
   things?

   Look in the Bible, the Bible,
   the B. I. B. L. E, the B. I. B. L. E,
   look in the Bible, the Bible.
   God's book he's given to you and me.

If you want to know why
God sent plagues of flies,
why Joshua sent out a team of spies,
how David wrote the Psalms we sing.
Where can you find all these amazing
   things?

533   Colin Buchanan based on Galatians 2:20

   I have been crucified with Christ
   and I no longer live,
   but Jesus Christ lives in me.
   I have been crucified with Christ.

The life I live in the body,
I live by faith in the Son of God,
who loved me and gave himself for me,
   2, 3, *(Clap)*

534   Amanda Lofts

I jump up and down and sing, 'I love you'.
Jump up and down and sing, 'I love you'.
I jump up and down and sing, 'I love you',
I love you, Jesus.

I stamp my feet and sing, 'I love you'.

I clap my hands and sing, 'I love you'.

I hop on one leg and sing, 'I love you'.

I wave my arms and sing, 'I love you'.

I dance all around and sing, 'I love you'.

535   Andy Read

I just want to love you,
I just want to worship you.
(Repeat x2)

There is nothing more I would rather do
than lift my head and sing, sing it out to
   you.
All that is inside, you know my feelings,
Lord, you are more powerful than all my
   life.
And Lord, you know the mysteries to all
   my life.

536   Margaret Carpenter

I know you're here beside me,
with ev'ry breath I take,
when night-time creeps into morning,
as the sun just begins to break,
I know you're with me, I know you're
   with me,
I feel the smile on your face, your warm
   embrace,
I know you are here with me.

537 The King's Church Creative Ministries

I'll clap, clap my hands to Jesus the King.
I'll stamp, stamp my feet because I love
    him.
I'll jump up and down, around I will spin,
I'll lift up my hands to him.

Oh hallelujah, oh hallelujah,
our praises we sing to the King.
Oh hallelujah, oh hallelujah,
with all of my heart I praise him.

538 James Wright

I look forward all year to Christmas time.
Oh, the joy and excitement that is mine;
Christmas trees in the windows shine so
    bright
like the glory of God that shone that
    night.

I look forward to Christmas all year
    round
for the joy of the season I have found;
Christmas carols that fill my heart with
    cheer.
Oh, how I really love this time of year.

For it's King Jesus' birthday,
that we rejoice in today.
Two thousand years of grace and power
and he is still mighty to save.

    Happy birthday, happy birthday,
    happy birthday to the King of kings.
      (Repeat)

539 J. Macpherson

I'm a kangaroo,
living in the zoo.
When I get up in the morning
this is what I do:
hip, hop, hippetty hop,
that's the way the kangaroos hop.
Hip, hop, hippetty hop,
that's the way we're made to be,
a part of God's creation.

I'm a budgie too,
living in the zoo.
When I get up in the morning
this is what I do:
tweet, tweet, tweedledee dee,
that's the way we sing in the tree.
Tweet, tweet, tweedledee dee,
that's the way we're made to be,
a part of God's creation.

I'm a black seal too,
living in the zoo.
When I get up in the morning
this is what I do:
flap, flap, flappetty flap,
that's the way we cheer and clap.
Flap, flap, flappetty flap,
that's the way we're made to be,
a part of God's creation.

I'm a hippo too,
living in the zoo.
When I get up in the morning
this is what I do:
splosh, splosh, sploshetty splosh,
that's the way we wallow and wash.
Splosh, splosh, sploshetty splosh,
that's the way we're made to be,
a part of God's creation.

Continued overleaf

I'm a person who
comes from a town near you.
When I get up in the morning
this is what I do:
rise, rise, rise and shine,
say 'Hello' to a friend of mine.
Rise, rise, rise and shine,
that's the way we're made to be,
a part of God's creation.

540 Capt. Alan J. Price, CA

I may be a child, but my worship is true;
an expression of all that I feel about
you.
Through music and song, through words
I will say:
Jesus, I'm trying to love you today.

*'Cos you've shown me how much you
love me,
I know deep inside I'm your special
child.
You've shown me how much you love
me,
I know deep inside I'm a child of the
Lord.*

I may be a child, but I know what I feel,
I want to obey you and show my faith is
real.
Stretch me and mould me, tell me what
and how,
Jesus, I want to serve you now.

I may be a child, but there's so much to
know,
it will take a lifetime to learn and to grow.
But Lord, I thank you now for all that I
can do,
as part of your family, living for you.

541 Doug Horley

I'm forever in your love,
I'm forever saved by grace.
You have chosen me and crowned me
with your love.
I'll forever trust in you,
I'll forever say you're good.
You are King of kings and I will worship
you.

La la la la la la, just want to thank you,
la la la la la la, just want to praise you,
la la la la la la, that I can live like this for
ever.

542 Andy Read

I'm gonna clap my hands and sing for joy,
I'm gonna clap my hands and sing for joy.
He has taken all my sins away.
(Repeat)

I will trust that Jesus will protect me
from the evil one;
no longer will I be afraid,
'cos his banner over me is wonderful love,
powerful love, incredible love,
whatever you can think of.

I'm gonna stamp my feet and shout
aloud . . .

I'm gonna jump and twist and wave my
hands . . .

543 Paul Crouch and David Mudie

I'm gonna let my light shine for you,
let it shine for you.
I'm gonna let my light shine for you
in ev'rything I do.

You put your light in me and I have been
 made new,
I'm gonna let, let it shine for you.
I'm not ashamed, I will not hide it,
I'm gonna let it blaze right out.
'Cos Jesus is the one who has supplied it
and he won't let the devil puff it out.

544   Martin Cooper

I'm gonna live for Jesus,
I'm gonna live for Jesus,
I'm gonna live for Jesus,
gonna do ev'rything he says.

If he tells me I should go,
then I won't say no:
gonna live for him.
If he tells me I should jump,
I'll ask him how high,
gonna touch the sky.

And every day I'm gonna pray,
I'm gonna live your way,
'cos I belong to you.
I'll give you ev'rything I am,
I'm gonna lift my hands,
'cos you deserve my praise.

Chant:
1, 2, 3, 4, 5, 6, 7, 8, I'm a friend of
 Jesus,
 I think that he's really great.

545   Ian Smale

I'm gonna say my prayers,
read my Bible ev'ry morning,
gonna get some fellowship,
witness ev'ry day.
(Repeat)

I am gonna pray ev'ry morning,
I am gonna pray ev'ry day.
(Repeat)

I am gonna read my Bible ev'ry morning,
I am gonna read my Bible ev'ry day.
(Repeat)

I am gonna fellowship ev'ry morning,
I am gonna fellowship ev'ry day.
(Repeat)

I am gonna witness ev'ry morning,
I am gonna witness ev'ry day.
(Repeat)

546   Jim Bailey

I'm gonna walk by faith, not by sight,
I'm gonna walk by faith, not by sight.
I'm gonna follow Jesus, and do what's
 right,
I'm gonna walk by faith, not by sight.

Jesus said, 'If you follow me,
you will never live in darkness.'
Jesus said, 'If you follow me,
you will live in the light.'

I'm gonna watch and pray every day.
I'm gonna watch and pray every day.
I'm gonna do ev'rything that I heard
 Jesus say.
I'm gonna watch and pray every day.

547 Steve Burnhope

I might not like my ears,
I might not like my nose,
I might not like my two front teeth,
my hair, my skin, my clothes.
I might think I'm too fat,
I might think I'm too thin,
too short, too tall, but warts 'n' all
God says I'm wonderfully made.

I'm wonderfully made, I'm wonderfully
 made,
no accident and no mistake, I'm
 wonderfully made,
I'm wonderfully made, I'm wonderfully
 made,
just as God the Father planned, I'm
 wonderfully made.

548 Ian Smale

I'm looking up to Jesus,
his face is shining beauty.
I'm feeling so unworthy,
yet his Spirit leads me on.
I'm looking up to Jesus,
his radiance surrounds me.
I feel so pure and clean,
a taste of heaven on earth.

549 Andrew and Pauline Pearson

I'm putting my trust in you,
I'm putting my trust in you,
I'm putting my trust in you,
Father God.

Doesn't matter how high the wind blows,
doesn't matter how hard it rains,
doesn't matter how loud it thunders,
I know you're here with me.

Doesn't matter how big the spiders,
doesn't matter how slippy the snakes,
doesn't matter how loud the dogs bark,
I know you're here with me.

Doesn't matter if I'm alone,
doesn't matter if friends leave me,
doesn't matter if I trip and fall,
I know you're here with me.

550 Andy Read

I'm saved, I'm saved,
it's alright, I've been born again.
And I'm saved, and I'm saved,
it's alright, I've been born again.
And I'm standing on the rock of Jesus
 Christ. (Repeat)

This is the truth I believe,
Jesus himself set me free
to trust and obey him in life.
That was the way it was meant to be.

This is the grace I believe;
it was his mercy to me
to show me his love and his light,
shining right into the darkest night.

551 Steve Burnhope

I'm so small in your world,
how come you even notice me?
I'm nothing big, I'm just a kid,
how come you are listening to me?

Jesus, you make me feel special,
'cause you've always time for me.
And when I pray, I may not always know
 what to say,
still you hear me, 'cause you love me
and you made me to be your child.

552 Andy Read

I'm walking in love, I'm walking in light.
I'm walking in the goodness of God
and the mercy of Jesus Christ.
I'm walking in love, I'm walking in light.
I'm walking in the goodness of God
and the mercy of Jesus Christ.

He has been good to me,
he has protected me,
so why should I be afraid?
He is the God of all gods,
he is the King of all kings
and right in my heart he'll stay.

553 Paul Harvey

I need your hand to guide me,
your presence, Lord, beside me;
there's no one else who could ever take
    your place.
I need your peace to still me,
your Holy Spirit to fill me;
there's no one else who could ever take
    your place.

I hide beneath your wings, my Father,
I owe you ev'rything, my Jesus,
send down your Spirit, Lord, and fill my
    soul again.
And I will run to you, my Father,
for there is none like you, my Jesus,
send down your Spirit, Lord, and I will
    praise your name.

554 Traditional Polish

Infant holy, infant lowly,
for his bed a cattle stall;
oxen lowing, little knowing
Christ the Babe is Lord of all.
Swift are winging
angels singing,
nowells ringing,
tidings bringing,
Christ the Babe is Lord of all,
Christ the Babe is Lord of all.

Flocks were sleeping, shepherds
    keeping
vigil till the morning new;
saw the glory, heard the story,
tidings of a gospel true.
Thus rejoicing, free from sorrow,
praises voicing, greet tomorrow,
Christ the Babe was born for you,
Christ the Babe was born for you!

trans. Edith Margaret Gellibrand Reed

555 Phil Chapman

In the beginning God made earth and
    heaven,
let's thank him and praise him as we
    should.
In the beginning God made earth and
    heaven
and God saw that it was very good.
This same creator is my Lord, my
    Saviour,
let's thank him and praise him as we
    should.

556 Christina Georgina Rossetti

In the bleak midwinter
frosty wind made moan,
earth stood hard as iron,
water like a stone;
snow had fallen, snow on snow,
snow on snow,
in the bleak midwinter,
long ago.

Our God, heav'n cannot hold him
nor earth sustain;
heav'n and earth shall flee away
when he comes to reign.
In the bleak midwinter
a stable-place sufficed
the Lord God almighty,
Jesus Christ.

Enough for him, whom cherubim
worship night and day,
a breastful of milk
and a mangerful of hay:
enough for him, whom angels
fall down before,
the ox and ass and camel
which adore.

Angels and archangels
may have gathered there,
cherubim and seraphim
thronged the air;
but only his mother
in her maiden bliss
worshipped the belovèd
with a kiss.

What can I give him,
poor as I am?
If I were a shepherd
I would bring a lamb;
if I were a wise man
I would do my part,
yet what I can I give him:
give my heart.

557 Dave Godfrey

In the morning I come downstairs,
eat my breakfast, say my prayers,
get my coat on and comb my hair,
then my mum, she calls to me,
'Come on!'
It's time to go:
boing, boing, boing, boing,
boing, boing, boing, boing,
boing, boing, boing, boing, boing,
boing, boing, boing, boing,
boing, boing, boing, boing,
boing, boing, boing, boing, boing.

After lunch on a normal day,
in the playground, out to play,
when my friends all come my way,
you can hear me shout to them,
'Come on!'
It's time to go,
boing, boing . . .

In the evening and after tea,
homework's done, I watch TV.
Little brother, he jumps on me,
then he whispers in my ears:
'Come on!'
It's time to go:
boing, boing . . .

Late at night as I rest my head,
I read my Bible in my bed.
I thank the Lord for what he's said,
then you hear me softly say:
'Come on!'
It's time to go z . . .

Boing, boing . . .

558 Judy Bailey

In the Spirit I rise, rise,
I rise to your call,
in the Spirit I rise, rise,
I rise up to your call.
(Repeat)

I have put my trust in God;
Father, Spirit, Son.
When he calls me to come
then I know I must respond,
I rise in the Spirit of love.

When things seem too hard for me
I will not give up.
You're the strength that I need,
power when the flesh is weak,
I rise in the Spirit of love.

I will live for you, my Lord,
my future's in your hand.
Here's my life for your plan,
take me, Jesus, here I am
I rise in the Spirit of love.

559 Andy Read

I really wanna thank you,
I wanna find a way to show my praise.
I really wanna clap you,
I wanna worship you in diff'rent ways.

I will sing, I will dance,
I will lift up holy hands.
I will wave before you
and say I want you in my life.
I will raise up my arms
to be held in your arms.
I will listen, I will listen, I will listen
for your voice.

560 Mike Burn

Is anyone in trouble?
They should pray;
is anyone happy?
Let them sing songs of praise.
(Repeat)

Is anyone sick?
Let them call for the elders
and the prayer of faith
will make the sick person well.
(Repeat)

This piece of advice can clearly be seen,
in James chapter five, thirteen to fifteen.

561 Doug Horley

Is there a plank in your eye?
big enough to walk on,
big enough to build a ship or
maybe start a bonfire.
Is there a plank stuck in your eye?
Stuck, stuck, stuck.
(Repeat)

Don't point a finger and say, Oy!
You're doing it wrong when hey, hey,
your own life is far from okay.
Don't point at the speck in your
    brother's eye,
when there's a whopping great plank in
    your own.

562 Edmund Hamilton Sears, alt.

It came upon the midnight clear,
that glorious song of old,
from angels bending near the earth
to touch their harps of gold:
'Peace on earth, goodwill to all,
from heav'n's all-gracious King!'
The world in solemn stillness lay
to hear the angels sing.

Still through the cloven skies they come,
with peaceful wings unfurled;
and still their heav'nly music floats
o'er all the weary world:
above its sad and lowly plains
they bend on hov'ring wing;
and ever o'er its Babel-sounds
the blessèd angels sing.

Yet with the woes of sin and strife
the world has suffered long;
beneath the angel-strain have rolled
two thousand years of wrong;
and warring humankind hears not
the love-song which they bring;
O hush the noise of mortal strife,
and hear the angels sing!

And ye, beneath life's crushing load,
whose forms are bending low,
who toil along the climbing way
with painful steps and slow:
look now! for glad and golden hours
come swiftly on the wing;
O rest beside the weary road,
and hear the angels sing.

For lo, the days are hast'ning on,
by prophets seen of old,
when with the ever-circling years
comes round the age of gold;
when peace shall over all the earth
its ancient splendours fling,
and all the world give back the song
which now the angels sing.

563 William Walsham How

It is a thing most wonderful,
almost too wonderful to be,
that God's own Son should come from
   heav'n,
and die to save a child like me.

And yet I know that it is true:
he chose a poor and humble lot,
and wept and toiled, and mourned and
   died,
for love of those who loved him not.

I sometimes think about the cross,
and shut my eyes, and try to see
the cruel nails and crown of thorns,
and Jesus crucified for me.

But even could I see him die,
I could but see a little part
of that great love which, like a fire,
is always burning in his heart.

I cannot tell how he could love
a child so weak and full of sin;
his love must be most wonderful,
if he could die my love to win.

It is most wonderful to know
his love for me so free and sure;
but 'tis more wonderful to see
my love for him so faint and poor.

And yet I want to love thee, Lord;
O light the flame within my heart,
and I will love thee more and more,
until I see thee as thou art.

564 John Lane

It really is a worry,
to stop and look around;
there's sadness, hate and madness,
a world that's upside down!
But Jesus came to show us
the change when God's in charge;
there's goodness, love and justice:
there's a new way: right side up!

Oh, right side up! It's a brand new
  way to live.
When others say 'Get even!' Jesus says
'Love and forgive!'
Oh, right side up! His love can change
  our hearts,
he'll take out the hate, we'll all be
  mates,
we'll make a brand new start!

When people say 'Fight harder!'
he says, 'Make peace instead!'
When people say 'Act smarter!'
he says, 'Just be true instead!'
When people get too greedy,
he says, 'Instead, be kind!'
When people think life's hopeless,
he says 'God is still in charge!'

When people say 'Look after
number one and get ahead!'
then Jesus says, 'Be happy,
obey what God has said!'
When people say 'It's nonsense!'
you gotta keep on Jesus' way.
His way will last for ever,
and it starts with us today.

Oh, right side up! It's a brand new
  way to live.
When other say 'Get even!' Jesus says
'Love and forgive!'
Oh, right side up! His love can change
  our hearts,
he'll take out the hate, we'll all be
  mates,
we'll make a brand new start!

565 Ian Smale

It's amazin' what praisin' can do.
It's amazin' what praisin' can do.
Join in and you'll see what it's been and
  done for me,
it's amazin' what praisin' can do.

It's amazin' what your mouth can do.
It's amazin' what your mouth can do.
It can shout, scream or cheer, as long as
  it's sincere,
it's amazin' what your mouth can do.

It's amazin' what clapping can do.
It's amazin' what clapping can do.
As my hands applaud they shout praise
  to the Lord,
it's amazin' what clapping can do.

It's amazin' what dancing can do.
It's amazin' what dancing can do.
King David employed it, and my feet
  enjoyed it,
it's amazin' what dancing can do.

566 Alison Fuggle

It's good to be together in all this
  stormy weather,
all snuggled safe together in God's boat:
to bob up and down all day, counting
  clouds above, and pray
we've followed God's instructions and
  we'll float!

It's good to be together though we've
  been rather cramped:
you could say our high spirits have
  been getting slightly damped!
We hope we'll soon be landing: can't
  wait to get the nod.
It's good to be together: yes, you and
  me and God!

It's good to be together, not sure if we
  will ever
get off the ark and walk out on dry
  land!
Though we've got our sea-legs now,
  we're all busy wond'ring how
the world will start brand new as God
  has planned.

567 Dave Cooke

It shouldn't take long to sing this song,
if you tell me where we are.
It's all about numbers in the Bible,
just tell me where we are.
From one to twelve is how it goes,
sing along and see it grow.

It shouldn't take long to sing this song,
if you tell me where we are.
One is for the only God, the only God
  Almighty.

Two for the testaments old and new.

Three for the Trinity, three in one.

Four for the gospels (Matthew, Mark,
  Luke, John).

Five thousand fed (five loaves, two fish).

Six wings of the Seraphim.

It shouldn't take long to sing this song,
if you tell me where we are.
It's all about numbers in the Bible,
just tell me where we are.
From one to twelve is how it goes,
sing along and see it grow.

Seven for the days that God made.

Eight for the people in Noah's Ark.

Nine fruits of the Spirit.

Ten for the Ten Commandments.

Eleven for the brothers of Joseph.

Twelve for the twelve disciples.

It shouldn't take long to sing this song,
if you tell me where we are.
It's all about numbers in the Bible,
just tell me where we are.
From one to twelve is how it goes,
sing along and see it grow.

568 Brian Howard

It's Jesus' joy that fills my heart;
it keeps me going when times get hard.
On eagles' wings he lifts me up;
his grace, amazing, is enough.
(Repeat)

It is your joy that fills my heart;
it keeps me going when times get hard.
On eagles' wings you lift me up;
your grace, amazing, is enough.

569 James Wright

It's the time to start the festive music,
it's the time to lift your voice and sing.
It's the time of praise and celebration,
it's the birthday of Jesus Christ the
King.

Ev'rybody praise him for sending us the
Son
from the Father's glory to earth for
ev'ryone.
Ev'rybody praise him, fill up your hearts
with joy,
ev'rybody worship the King.

Ev'rybody praise him for Christ has
come to earth,
ev'rybody praise him on this, the
Saviour's birth.
Ev'rybody praise him, fill up your hearts
with joy,
ev'rybody worship the King.

Hallelujah, hallelujah the angels sang.
Hallelujah, hallelujah, goodwill to man.
Hallelujah, hallelujah, Emmanuel,
God with man to dwell.

570 Dave Cooke

It's time to say we're sorry
for all the bad things we have done.
No need to worry,
God forgives us through his Son.
It doesn't really matter how bad we've
been
or what we've said to each other:
he can wipe the whole slate clean
when we honestly ask our Father to
forgive us,
forgive us, forgive us, forgive us.

Thank you, Lord, for making us clean
and sending Jesus to save us.
Thank you that no matter how bad it
seems,
you're there in our heart, right there,
always ready to forgive us,
forgive us, forgive us.
Thank you for forgiving us,
thank you for forgiving us.

571 Joy Webb

It was on a starry night when the hills
were bright.
Earth lay sleeping, sleeping calm and still;
then in a cattle shed, in a manger bed
a boy was born, King of all the world.

And all the angels sang for him,
the bells of heaven rang for him;
for a boy was born, King of all the
world.
And all the angels sang for him,
the bells of heaven rang for him;
for a boy was born, King of all the
world.

Continued overleaf

Soon the shepherds came that way,
  where the baby lay,
and were kneeling, kneeling by his side.
And their hearts believed again, for the
  peace of men;
for a boy was born, King of all the world.

  And all the angels sang for him,
  the bells of heaven rang for him;
  for a boy was born, King of all the
    world.
  And all the angels sang for him,
  the bells of heaven rang for him;
  for a boy was born, King of all the
    world.

On a starry night, on a starry night.

572 Susie Hare

I've got a friend called Jesus
who is with me wherever I go.
I've got a friend called Jesus
and I want ev'ryone to know
that I will never be without him,
because his love for me
is much, much higher than the mountain
and much, much deeper than the sea.

573 G. W. Cooke

I've got that joy, joy, joy, joy
down in my heart, (where?)
down in my heart, (where?)
down in my heart.
I've got that joy, joy, joy, joy
down in my heart, (where?)
down in my heart to stay.

And I'm so happy, so very happy;
I've got the love of Jesus in my heart.
And I'm so happy, so very happy;
I've got the love of Jesus in my heart.

I've got the peace that passes
  understanding
down in my heart, (where?)
down in my heart, (where?)
down in my heart.
I've got the peace that passes
  understanding
down in my heart, (where?)
down in my heart to stay.

574 Phil Overton

I've never been to a circus to watch the
  clowns perform.
I've never seen a trapeze man, but I've
  heard about it all.
I've never seen a lion tamer, although
  I've heard what the children say.
But I'm learning to walk on a tightrope
  and
I'm getting better every day.

  And I don't even need a safety net,
  because Jesus is watching me.
  And although I haven't quite got it yet,
  I know that he's close by me.
  He throws down a line in an evil world
  for all who will trust and obey,
    and so I'm learning to walk on a
      tightrope
  and I'm getting better every day.

When a preacher told me about it,
I thought he must be mad!
I said, 'I could never keep it up'
but deep inside I was sad.
He said, ' You don't have to do a thing –
just trust in Jesus and pray.'
So I'm learning to walk on a tightrope
   and
I'm getting better every day.

The world around has gone crazy.
It gets more like a circus ev'ry day
and I long to rise far above it
and walk on a better way.
Well, Jesus helped me to do it –
all I had to do was pray.
And I'm learning to walk on a tightrope
and I'm getting better every day.

575 Andy Read

I wanna give you,
I wanna give you,
I wanna give all my love to you.
I wanna give you,
I wanna give you,
I wanna give all my love to you.

Walking down the street,
running in the park,
swimming in the pool,
wanna talk to you.
Riding in the woods,
splashing in the stream,
playing in my room,
I wanna talk to you.

576 Margaret Carpenter

I want my life to be pleasing to you,
help me to stand for the things that are
   true,
turning my back on the wrong that I
   know,
standing for right ev'rywhere that I go.
There'll be mountains to climb,
there'll be heartache at times,
and the pathway won't always be easy,
there'll be tears on the way
but to life I will say,
God's on my side come what may.

577 Chris Jackson

I want to be like you, Lord Jesus,
I want to be like you.
And I want to follow you, Lord Jesus,
I want to follow you.

Fill me with your Holy Spirit,
fill me with your love.
'Cos I want to be like you, Lord Jesus,
I want to be like you.

Hold me in your arms, Lord Jesus,
keep me close to you.
'Cos I want to follow you, Lord Jesus,
I want to follow you.

578 Capt. Alan J. Price, CA

I will always follow Jesus,
I will always follow him.
Ev'rything I do for Jesus
will bring happiness to him.
I will make time just for Jesus,
I will listen and obey.
I will always try to please him,
by the things I do each day.

579 Andy Read

I will believe in Jesus,
I will believe in the cross where he died.
I will believe in Jesus 'cos he's alive!
(Repeat)

I will trust him to be faithful
and to answer me when I pray.
He rewards those who will seek him
and discover his great love!

He will keep us and protect us
from the evil around this world.
He will fill us with the power
to tell others of his great love!

580 Ian Smale

I will bend down and touch my knees
and then I'll touch my toes.
Now I'll stand up straight again
and hold on to my nose.
I cover my eyes with my hands
so I cannot see,
then reach my hands up in the air
for God created me.
God created me,
God created me.
I'll reach my hands up in the air
for God created me.

581 Unknown

I will bless the Lord, he is worthy to be
    praised.
I will bless the Lord, he is worthy to be
    praised.
I will bless the Lord, he is worthy to be
    praised.
He is worthy, worthy to be praised.

I will lift my voice, he is worthy to be
    praised. *(x3)*
He is worthy, worthy to be praised.

I will lift my hands, he is worthy to be
    praised. *(x3)*
He is worthy, worthy to be praised.

I will lift his name, he is worthy to be
    praised. *(x3)*
He is worthy, worthy to be praised.

582 Mike Burn

I will lift up the name of the Lord,
I will lift up the name of the Lord,
I will lift up the name of the one who
    lifted me.
He took my feet from the slippery clay,
set them on a solid rock to stay,
I will lift up the name of the one who
    lifted me.

Oh, I praise you, Jesus, for you always
    hear my cry.
Every day that you give me breath
I'm gonna lift your name on high.

583 Nick Harding

I will not be afraid of what I hear,
I will not be afraid of what I see,
I will not be afraid of anything
'cos I know God's with me.

Like Moses on the mountain,
or Paul upon the sea,
or John the Baptist speaking out,
I know that God's with me.

Like Mary with the angel,
or Peter when set free,
or David hiding in a cave,
I know that God's with me.

Like Noah in the flooding,
or Joshua's victory,
or Esther standing up for truth,
I know that God's with me.

Like a father's mercy on his own little
    ones,
so the Lord has shown me compassion.
Why should I worry, why should I fret?
On my Father's love I can depend.
On my Father's love I can depend.
I will praise you with all of my heart,
soul, and mind.
Oh, I will praise you with
all of my heart, soul, and mind.

584 Brian Howard

I will praise you with all of my heart,
soul, and mind.
Oh, I will praise you with all of my heart,
soul, and mind.

All the cattle on a thousand hills,
all the fishes in the deep blue sea.
All the gold in the earth below,
all of this my Father owns.
All of this, yes, my Father owns.

Precious pearls, all gems and jewels,
all the fields and all the fossil fuel.
All the cars and all the microchips,
he made the things they made them with.
He made the things they made them with.

Bless the Lord now, O my soul.
Bless the Lord now, O my soul.
And forget none of his benefits.
And forget none of his benefits.
Who heals me and forgives my sins.
Who heals me and forgives my sins.
With all of my heart now, I will praise him.
With all of my heart now, I will praise him.
Oh, I will praise you with all of my heart,
soul and mind.
Oh, I will praise you with all of my heart,
soul and mind.

585 Jennifer Atkinson and Robin Mark

Jesus, all for Jesus;
all I am and have and ever hope to be.
(Repeat)

All of my ambitions, hopes and plans,
I surrender these into your hands.
(Repeat)

   For it's only in your will that I am free.
   For it's only in your will that I am free.

586 Roger Jones from *Stargazers* (1976)

Jesus, baby Jesus,
you're just a small babe.
Jesus, how we love you,
though you're just a babe.
Saviour, as you're sleeping,
Saviour, are you mine?
Jesus, though a baby,
Jesus, you're divine.

587 Michael Frye

Jesus, be the centre,
be my source, be my light,
Jesus.
Jesus, be the centre,
be my hope, be my song,
Jesus.

Be the fire in my heart,
be the wind in these sails,
be the reason that I live,
Jesus, Jesus.

Jesus, be my vision,
be my path, be my guide,
Jesus.

588 Susan Warner

Jesus bids us shine
with a pure, clear light,
like a little candle
burning in the night.
In this world is darkness:
so we must shine,
you in your small corner,
and I in mine.

Jesus bids us shine
first of all for him;
well he sees and know it,
if our light grows dim.
He looks down from heaven
to see us shine,
you in your small corner,
and I in mine.

Jesus bids us shine,
then, for all around;
many kinds of darkness
in the world abound:
sin, and want and sorrow;
so we must shine,
you in your small corner,
and I in mine.

589 J. Macpherson

Jesus born in Bethlehem,
born in a cattle stall.
Jesus born in Bethlehem,
born in a cattle stall.
That's the Holy Gospel,
good news for one and all.
Jesus born in Bethlehem,
born in a cattle stall.

Jesus called disciples too,
twelve of them in all.
Jesus called disciples too,
twelve of them in all.
That's the Holy Gospel,
good news for one and all.
Jesus called disciples too,
twelve of them in all.

Jesus healed the sick and lame,
when in faith they called.
Jesus healed the sick and lame
when in faith they called.
That's the Holy Gospel,
good news for one and all.
Jesus healed the sick and lame
when in faith they called.

Jesus sailed upon the sea,
calmed the raging storm.
Jesus sailed upon the sea,
calmed the raging storm.
That's the Holy Gospel,
good news for one and all.
Jesus sailed upon the sea,
calmed the raging storm.

Jesus died upon the cross,
carried the sins of all.
Jesus died upon the cross,
carried the sins of all.
That's the Holy Gospel,
good news for one and all.
Jesus died upon the cross,
carried the sins of all.

Jesus rose to life again,
he is our living Lord.
Jesus rose to life again,
he is our living Lord.
That's the Holy Gospel,
good news for one and all.
Jesus rose to life again,
he is our living Lord.

590 Jennie Flack

Jesus came to make things new.
He can start with you,
yes he can.
Jesus came to make things new.
If you let him, he can start with you.

There seems to be so much wrong and
   sadness around.
People always seem to spoil good
   things.
There seems to be so much wrong and
   sadness around.
Jesus came to make things new.

He makes good things better.
He can change things altogether.
From right where you are,
he's not very far away.

591 W. J. Mathams

Jesus, friend of little children, be a
   friend to me;
take my hand, and ever keep me close
   to thee.
Teach me how to grow in goodness,
   daily as I grow;
you have been a child and surely you
   will know,
you will know.

Step by step, O lead me onward, upward
   into youth;
wiser, stronger, still becoming in your
   truth.
Never leave me, nor forsake me; ever be
   my friend;
for I need you from life's dawning to its
   end,
to its end.

592 Derek Llewellyn

Jesus gave ev'ry one of us a song to
   sing. *(x3)*
Oh! there's nobody else like Jesus.

He loves each and every single one of
   us. *(x3)*
Oh! there's nobody else like Jesus.

So tell ev'rybody else around the world.
   (x3)
Oh! there's nobody else like Jesus.

So the whole world can come along and
   worship him. *(x3)*
Oh! there's nobody else like Jesus.

593 Jennie Flack

Jesus is here, Jesus is there,
Jesus is even right over there.
He has no trouble being ev'rywhere;
that's how God meant it to be.
The farthest galaxy, deepest ocean,
the loneliest place; he is there.
Nowhere in the universe he cannot be;
he is there ev'rywhere loving you.
No place in the sky is not higher.
No hole in the earth, he's not deeper still.
No desert so wide he can't stand astride it,
he is there ev'rywhere loving you.
He is there ev'rywhere loving you.

594 Steve Burnhope

Jesus is my friend, closer than a brother,
loves me like no other, always there for
  me.
Jesus is my friend, he loves and protects
  me,
never will forget me, best friend there
  could be.

595 Colin Buchanan

Jesus is the mighty, mighty King,
Jesus is the mighty, mighty King.
God made him the boss of ev'rything,
and Jesus is the mighty, mighty King.

Now *(name)* is not the boss, uh uh!
(name) is not the boss, uh uh!
(name) is not the boss, uh uh!
Jesus is the boss, 'cos …

Now you are not the boss, uh uh!
I am not the boss, uh uh!
They are not the boss, uh uh!
Jesus is the boss, 'cos …

Jesus is the mighty, mighty,
Jesus is the mighty, mighty,
Jesus is the mighty, mighty King.
  Yes sir!

596 Chris Jackson and Jill Hoffmann
based on Hebrews 13:8

Jesus is the same, Jesus is the same,
  (x2)
yesterday, today, for ever,
Jesus is the same.

He's the healer and deliv'rer,
he's the Saviour of the world.
Over all that he's created, he is Lord.
He's the master and the teacher,
he's our ever-faithful friend,
and his love will never, never, never end.

He's the Alpha and Omega,
the beginning and the end.
From the past into the future, he is Lord.
Knowing ev'rything about us,
still he loves us just the same,
so we'll give him all our love and praise
  his name.

597 Traditional

Jesus is the Saviour that I love to know.
Heaven is the haven that I'm going to.
Jesus is the captain who now leads my
  life.
Unworthy as I am, I know he came to
  save
a sinner such as me, a sinner such as you,
he came to save from the grave.

*For God so loved the world
that he gave his one and only Son.
That whosoever believes in him
should not perish, but have
    everlasting life.*

Sometimes when you're feeling all alone
    and blue,
Jesus will come in and he will pull you
    through.
And if you start a-thinking you need
    Jesus too,
come on sinner, come to him, he died
    for you.
A sinner such as me, a sinner such as
    you,
he came to save from the grave.

598 Capt. Alan J. Price, CA

Jesus, it's amazing, amazing but it's true;
there's no one else in history who's ever
    been like you.

You taught and showed what God was
    like,
did nothing else but good,
but they took you and they killed you
on a cross made out of wood.

    *It's a shame, but it's true;
    to think of all they did
    to try and get rid of you.*
    (Repeat)

They sealed your body in a tomb,
and thought that was 'goodbye'
but God brought you back to life,
never more to die.

    *It's a shame, but it's true;
    to think of all they did
    to try and get rid of you.*
    (Repeat)

Some have died for others,
and some have done great things,
but Jesus, you are different,
you're the King of kings.

    *I'm so glad that it's true;
    there's no one else in all the world
    who's ever been like you.*
    (Repeat)

You're not just some great teacher,
or a prophet, that is true,
you're the Son of God, the rescuer,
and I believe in you!

    *I'm so glad that it's true;
    there's no one else in all the world
    who's ever been like you.*
    (Repeat)

599 Neil Davidson

    *Jesus, Jesus, how you love me,
    Jesus, Jesus, how you care:
    I will try to love and trust you,
    follow you ev'ry day.*

Jesus you are with me,
each and ev'ry day:
even when I'm all alone,
you will hold my hand.

Even in the playground,
playing with my friends,
I know someone's watching me,
happy to see me here.

Jesus, you're my hero,
Jesus, you're my friend:
ev'ry day I grow and grow,
I'll love you even more.

600 Paul Oakley

Jesus, lover of my soul,
all-consuming fire is in your gaze.
Jesus, I want you to know
I will follow you all my days.
For no one else in history is like you,
and history itself belongs to you.
Alpha and Omega, you have loved me,
and I will share eternity with you.

It's all about you, Jesus,
and all this is for you,
for your glory and your fame.
It's not about me,
as if you should do things my way;
you alone are God,
and I surrender to your ways.

601 Sharon E. Ward

Jesus made my body, Jesus made my
soul,
Jesus made my spirit and he made me
whole.
Jesus made my body from my head to
my feet,
put me all together and he made me
neat.
In the image of the Father, the image of
the Son,
though we all look different we all are
one.
Jesus made my body from my head to
my feet,
put me all together and he made me
neat.

602 John Hardwick

Jesus never, never, never turned
anyone away.
No! No! No!
Jesus never, never, never turned
anyone away.

He welcomed the young, he welcomed
the old,
he never left anyone out in the cold.
He welcomed the hungry, he welcomed
the lame:
Jesus welcomes ev'ryone the same.

He never, never, never, never,
never, never, never, never,
never, never, never, never,
never! turned anyone away.
No, he never, never, never, never,
never, never, never, never,
never, never, never, never,
never! turned anyone way.

603 Chris Jackson

Jesus said, 'I have come
that they may have life,
that they may have L. I. F. E!'
Jesus said, 'I have come
that they may have life,
and have it to the full.'

604 Ian Smale

Jesus said 'Let little children come unto me
and do not ever hinder them,
for the kingdom of God belongs to such
as these,'
says the fourteenth verse of Mark in
chapter ten.
And anyone who won't receive the
kingdom of God
like a little child who wants their life
made clean,
will never enter it, is the truth that Jesus
taught.
From Mark in chapter ten and verse
fifteen.

605 John Hardwick

Jesus said 'Let the children come unto me.
Do not hinder them, let them come to me.'

Girls
*Let the little children, let the little
children,
let the little children come unto me.
(Repeat)*

Boys (not first time)
*For the kingdom, the kingdom, the
kingdom of God,
yes the kingdom, the kingdom, the
kingdom of God,
for the kingdom, the kingdom, the
kingdom of God
belongs to such as these.
(Repeat)*

The disciples tried to turn them away,
but he said 'Let them come to me.'
They thought they'd only get in the way,
but he said 'Let them come to me.'

Girls
*Let the little children, let the little
children,
let the little children come unto me.
(Repeat)*

Boys
*For the kingdom, the kingdom, the
kingdom of God,
yes the kingdom, the kingdom, the
kingdom of God,
for the kingdom, the kingdom, the
kingdom of God
belongs to such as these.
(Repeat)*

He sat one down upon his knee
and said, 'Let them come to me.'
Children have the right to see!
He said 'Let them come to me.'

606 Jennie Flack

Jesus said something wonderful,
Jesus said something true.
What he said you should listen to,
'cause what he said was meant for you.

I am the Light of the World,
don't live in darkness.
I am the Light of the World,
come follow me.
I am the Light of the World,
do what I tell you,
and together we'll live,
together we'll live, together we'll live,
together we'll live the right way.

607 Andy Read

Jesus wants all of me,
Jesus wants all of me,
Jesus wants all of me,
that's what he wants.
(Repeat)

My heart, my mind, my hands, my feet,
my ears, my nose, my eyes, my teeth,
my arms, my legs, my toes, my knees,
Jesus wants all of me.

608 Amanda Lofts

Jesus was out for a walk one day
when people brought their babies and
    children his way.
His friends told them off and said, 'Go
    away'
but Jesus said, 'No, these children must
    stay.'
Because Jesus (Jesus) loves the children
    (children).
Yes, Jesus (Jesus) cares for them (for
    them).

609 Nick and Trish Parrans-Smith

Jesus, we dance for joy,
we lift our hands and we praise.
O Lord Jesus, King of kings,
we give you honour and glory and
    praise.

Ev'ry day I do so many things,
sometimes they're not what you want
    me to do.
Jesus Christ, I want to follow you,
I want to be more like you in all I do.

Ev'ry day I say so many things,
sometimes they're not what you want
    me to say.
Jesus Christ, I want to follow you,
I want to be more like you ev'ry day.

610 John Hardwick

Jesus went out of his way, out of his
    way,
out of his way to help others!
Jesus went out of his way, out of his
    way,
out of his way to do right!
So let's go out of our way, out of our
    way,
out of our way to help others!
So let's go out of our way, out of our
    way,
out of our way to do right!

When I was hungry did you feed me?
When I was thirsty did you give me a
    drink?
An outsider, did you welcome me
or did you turn me away?

When I had no clothes, did you clothe
    me?
When I was so sick did you look after
    me?
When in prison, did you visit me
or did you turn me away?

611 Capt. Alan J. Price, CA

Jesus, you knew me right from the start;
Jesus, you chose me, set me apart.
You want the best for me,
I know that is true, and I say 'yes' to you,
I'll follow you.
(Repeat)

Jesus, you came and you showed us again
how God loves us.
Jesus, you came and you taught us again
we must turn from our sin,
we must turn to him.

Jesus, you knew me right from the start;
Jesus, you chose me, set me apart.
You want the best for me,
I know that is true, and I say 'yes' to
    you,
this is my 'yes' to you,
oh I say 'yes' to you,
I'll follow you.

612 Sophie Larbalestier and Suzi de Faye

Jesus, you're lovely, Jesus, you're mine.
Ev'rywhere I go you're with me
all the time.

And I praise your name, and I praise
    your name.
You are the mighty God, the living Word,
master of ev'rything, you are the Lord.

And I love your name, and I love your
    name.
You are the Prince of Peace, Emmanuel,
everlasting Father, you are the Lord.

613 Andrew and Pauline Pearson

Jesus, your name is wonderful,
Jesus, your name is truth.
Jesus, your name is powerful,
Jesus, we love you.

In your name the blind will see.
In your name the lame will dance.
In your name we are set free
to follow you.
In your name, your powerful name.

614 Capt. Alan J. Price, CA

Keep on going, keep on growing,
keep on knowing Jesus better.
Keep on going, keep on growing,
keep on knowing Jesus better.

Let your roots go deeper into Jesus
and let him be the foundation for your life;
be strong in your faith, (huh!)
just as you've been learning,
overflow with your praise,
give the honour all to God.

Like a tree, be fruitful for Jesus,
and as living stones be built up in the
    Lord;
let the Bible be your guide, (yes!)
just as you've been learning,
overflow with your love,
live to please our Father God.

615 Steve Burnhope

King David was a worshipper beyond
    compare,
as they say 'en français', 'extraordinaire!'
The queen said, 'How undignified!' but
    he didn't care,
'cos this is what he said as he gracefully
    leapt in the air.

Continued overleaf

'Let's go dancing, we're all gonna go dancing,
movin' an' a-groovin' in praise before the Lord.
Let's go dancing, we're all gonna go dancing,
we're gonna dance in praise before the Lord.*

King David knew that dancing was the thing to do,
pleasing to God, and pretty good for you,
give it a try and you'll see that it's true,
David was right when he said this is what you should do.

616   Ruth and Trevor Ranger

2 part round

Sung twice by all
King, King, King of the hill,
showing ev'rybody that God loves us still.
King, King, King of the hill,
in life and in death
he's the King of the hill.

Part 1 (3rd and 4th times only)
King, King, King of the hill,
showing ev'rybody that God loves us still.
King, King, King of the hill,
in life and in death
he's the King of the hill.

Part 2 (every time)
Up upon the hillside, people there all day,
Jesus showing the way.
Up upon the hillside,
we must listen still,
Jesus, King of the hill.

617   Susanna Levell

King Nebuchadnezzar made
an image of gold,
he gathered all the people round
and this is what he told them:
'When you hear the sound
of the music being played,
Shout: you must bow down
to the image I've made!'

*Oh! Shadrach, Meshach and Abednego
were being protected by the Lord,
you know,
they served no one other than their
God alone,
the true and living God.*

King Nebuchadnezzar saw that
they did not bow,
he called his strongest soldiers
and began to tell them how
to tie the three men up
and then throw them in the fire.
Shout: 'You must make sure that
the flames burn much higher!'

King Nebuchadnezzar,
when he looked in the fire,
he jumped with amazement
and began to question why
there was an extra man
in the fire with the three.
Shout: 'Your God has saved you
and now you are free!'

618   Doug Horley

King of love, praise you,
King of love, worship you,
King of love, thank you,
I'm treasure in your eyes.
(Repeat)

I know my heart
will love you for ever,
I know your word,
I'll always be your child.
I know my soul
is safe for eternity,
'cos you hold me close
 in your arms.
(Repeat from beginning)

Gonna give you all the praise I can,
gonna give you all the thanks I can,
in your arms, I will be,
King of love holding me.

Gonna give you all the love I can,
gonna give you all the praise I can,
in your arms I will be,
King of love holding me.
Gonna give you all the praise I can,
gonna give you all the thanks I can,
King of love, King of love, I worship
    you.

> *King of love, praise you,*
> *King of love, worship you,*
> *King of love, thank you,*
> *I'm treasure in your eyes.*

619 Garrie-John Barnes

> *La la la la la la la la la la la la la la la*
> *la la la la la la la*
> *la la la la la la la la la la la la la la la*
> *la la la la la la la.*

We will rejoice in the Lord,
rejoice in the Lord,
rejoice in the Lord always!
We will rejoice in the Lord,
rejoice in the Lord,
rejoice in the Lord always!

We will clap hands to the Lord,
clap hands to the Lord,
clap hands to the Lord always!
We will clap hands to the Lord,
clap hands to the Lord,
clap hands to the Lord always!

We will sing praise to the Lord,
sing praise to the Lord,
sing praise to the Lord always!
We will sing praise to the Lord,
sing praise to the Lord,
sing praise to the Lord always!

620 Capt. Alan J. Price, CA

> *La la la la la, we clap our hands and*
>   *sing;*
> *la la la la la, Jesus is our King.*
> *La la la la la, we clap our hands and*
>   *sing;*
> *la la la la la, Jesus is our King.*

He doesn't need a palace,
where we can stand and stare.
He doesn't need a big posh car
to take him ev'rywhere. (No!)
Through the Holy Spirit
at work in you and me,
he's building his Kingdom
wherever we may be!

Oh yeah! Oh yeah! *(x2)*

He doesn't make us serve him,
like a servant should;
he doesn't say it's easy
to do what's right and good. (No!)
When we know he loves us,
we want to love him too;
and 'cos we want to be like him
that's just what we do!

Continued overleaf

Oh yeah! Oh yeah! *(x2)*

La la la la la, we clap our hands and
sing;
la la la la la, Jesus is our King.
La la la la la, we clap our hands and
sing;
la la la la la, Jesus is our King.
(Repeat)

Alleluia, we will clap our hands.

We will dance our feet.

We will shout Amen!
Praise the Lord!

621   Andy Read

Lean to the left, lean to the right
just to make sure my shoes are on tight.
Reach to the floor, reach to the sky;
I'm gonna get ready, it's nearly time.

I'm gonna get fit to run the race,
I don't wanna fall flat on my face.
See my eyes, see me smile,
I'm now gonna jog for a thousand miles.

Running after you (gonna make it),
running after you (take me through it).
Running after you (gonna make it),
running after you (I can take it).

Jump to the left, jump to the right
just to make sure my legs are on tight.
Turning around, touching the ground,
I wouldn't stop for a thousand pounds.

622   Chris Jackson

Let all the earth give praise to the
Father,
let all the earth give praise to our God.
Let all the earth rejoice and praise the
Lord.

623   Matt Redman

Let ev'rything that, ev'rything that,
ev'rything that has breath,
praise the Lord.
Let ev'rything that, ev'rything that,
ev'rything that has breath,
praise the Lord.

Praise you in the morning,
praise you in the evening,
praise you when I'm young and when
    I'm old.
Praise you when I'm laughing,
praise you when I'm grieving,
praise you ev'ry season of the soul.
If we could see how much you're worth,
your pow'r, your might, your endless
    love,
then surely we would never cease to
    praise.

Praise you in the heavens,
joining with the angels,
praising you for ever and a day.
Praise you on the earth now,
joining with creation,
calling all the nations to your praise.
If they could see …

624 Ian Smale

Count: *One, two, three, four.*

Let's count to four and count our
    blessings,
God has given us so much.
Let's name four things and then say
    'thank you'
for the Lord is good to us.

Count: *One, two, three, four.*

Let's count to four and pray for others,
God has given us so much.
Let's name four people we can pray for,
for the Lord is good to us.

625 Alison Moon

Let's praise God together,
let us clap and praise the Lord,
for he loves to hear us,
he is King for evermore.

Jesus, holy is your name,
high above all others,
pow'r and glory belong to you.

Let's praise God together,
let us dance and praise the Lord,
for he loves to hear us,
he is King for evermore.

Jesus, mighty is your name,
high above all others,
pow'r and glory belong to you.

626 Dave Bilbrough

Let the chimes of freedom ring
all across the earth;
lift your voice in praise to him
and sing of all his worth,
and sing of all his worth.

Open wide your prison doors
to greet the Lord of life;
songs of triumph fill the air,
Christ Jesus is alive,
Christ Jesus is alive.

Let all the people hear the news
of the One who comes to save:
he's the Lord of all the universe,
and for ever he shall reign.

In ev'ry corner of the earth
to ev'ry tribe and tongue,
make known that God so loved this world
that he gave his only Son,
he gave his only Son.

Spread the news and make it plain:
he breaks the pow'r of sin.
Jesus died and rose again,
his love will never end,
his love will never end.

Let all the people hear the news
of the One who comes to save:
he's the Lord of all the universe,
and for ever he shall reign.
And for evermore and for evermore,
and for evermore he shall reign.
And for evermore and for evermore,
and for evermore he shall reign.

He will return in majesty
to take his rightful place
as King of all eternity,
the Name above all names,
the Name above all names.

627 James Wright

Let there be singing, songs of rejoicing;
let there be joy throughout the earth.
Let ev'ry nation sing of God's salvation;
this is the season to rejoice.

From heaven to earth you came,
the Son of God to reign.
God's gift of everlasting love.
From heaven to earth to dwell,
Jesus, Emmanuel.
God's gift of everlasting love.

Hallelujah, hallelujah,
God with us has come to dwell.
Hallelujah, hallelujah,
God with us, Emmanuel.

628 John Burland and John Jacobs

Let the Spirit dwell within our hearts,
to celebrate the wonder of our God.
As we reach out together
and find our strength in you,
come share the gifts of the Spirit.
(Repeat)

629 Chris Jackson and Jill Hoffman

Let us be grateful and worship God
in a way that will please him,
with reverence and awe.

Let us worship, let us worship,
let us worship with reverence and awe.

630 Julia Abrahams

Let your kingdom come, let your
* kingdom come.*
Let your kingdom come, O Lord, let
* your kingdom come.*
Let your kingdom come, let your
* kingdom come,*
let your kingdom, let your kingdom,
* let your kingdom come.*

The kingdom's like a tiny seed (let your
  kingdom come)
that grows into a mighty tree (let your
  kingdom come),
the birds of the air nest in that tree (let
  your kingdom come).
Let your kingdom, let your kingdom, let
  your kingdom come.

The kingdom's like a pinch of yeast (let
  your kingdom come)
that spreads throughout a mighty feast
  (let your kingdom come).
From a pinch of yeast to mighty feast
  (let your kingdom come).
Let your kingdom, let your kingdom, let
  your kingdom come.

The kingdom's like a rare, rare pearl (let
  your kingdom come),
the rarest pearl in all the world (let your
  kingdom come).
Men sell their wealth to get that pearl
  (let your kingdom come).
Let your kingdom, let your kingdom, let
  your kingdom come.

Let your kingdom come, let your
*   kingdom come.*
Let your kingdom come, O Lord, let
*   your kingdom come.*
Let your kingdom come, let your
*   kingdom come,*
let your kingdom, let your kingdom, let
*   your kingdom come.*
(Repeat)

631   Christine Dalton

Liar, liar, pants on fire,
Mum is mad, who's been bad?
Liar, liar, pants on fire,
Mum is mad, who's been bad?

Who put play-doh on Mum's carpet?
Who put scribble on Mum's wall?
Who gave the cat a brand new haircut?
Who forgot to go to school?
Satan is a liar, liars feed the fire.
It is his desire just to hear you say:

I, I, I, I didn't do it, no, Mum, honestly!
I, I, I, I didn't do it. Could it be Mister
   Nobody?
(Repeat)

Who put soap suds in the fish tank?
Who lost Dad's remote control?
Who put a football through the window,
trying hard to score a goal?
It is up to you, will you tell the truth?
God is proud of you when he hears you
   say:

I, I, I, I didn't mean it, no, Mum, honestly!
I, I, I, I didn't mean it, sorry Mum, for
   what I've done.
(Repeat)

632   Robin Mann

Lord, hear my praying,
listen to me;
you know there's evil in what I see.
I know I'm part of all that is wrong.
Still, won't you hear my sorrowing song?

Children are crying, hungry for food;
sick from disease – God, are you good?
People are homeless, lost and alone:
God, are you hiding?
Where have you gone?

Why do the rich ones steal from the poor?
Why do they build their weapons of war?
How can you stand the torture and pain,
hope disappearing, freedom in chains?

Jesus, remind us that you are found
with those who cry,
with those who are bound;
where there is suff'ring, you will be there –
help us to follow, Lord, hear my prayer.

633   Tim Moyler and Donna Vann

Lord, help me to tell your story
to those who've never heard,
how you lived and died for us;
you are the way to God.

I want to go, Lord, in your power,
telling the story of your name.
I want to say what you said,
do what you did, tell the world the
*   reason you came.*

Lord, help me to tell my story
of what you've done for me.
Give me courage, Lord, to say
how you have set me free.

Continued overleaf

I want to go, Lord, in your power,
telling the story of your name.
I want to say what you said,
do what you did, tell the world the
reason you came.

Rap:
You came down from heaven, born in a
stable,
grew as a child in the wisdom of God.
Teaching and preaching, healing and
blessing,
stirring up anger; you died on a cross.
Sealed in a tomb; burst from the grave;
ascended to heaven and you're coming
again!
I will live out your story to the glory of
your name. *(x4)*

Lord, so many live in darkness,
lost in an endless night.
Help them search and find you, Lord,
and fill them with your light.

634 Lynn Howson

Lord, I feel the heartbeat of your love
beating for me.
Lord, I hear you calling my name,
calling to me.

And I am ready to receive your love,
and I am ready to respond to your call.
Lord, make me ready for your fire to fall.

Your Spirit is stirring in us,
fill us once again:
let our hearts burn with a passion
to glorify your name.

635 Ian Smale

Lord, I need to know you love me,
Lord, I need to know you care;
in the times I feel rejected,
I need to know you're there.
God says, 'Listen my little child,
I'm a father who'll never leave you,
and though all your friends may fail you,
you can always trust in me.
For you're priceless and you're precious
and your value cannot be measured,
you're an heir to my kingdom,
you're in my chosen family.'

636 Dave Godfrey

Lord, I wanna pause, pause in your
presence;
Lord, I wanna be still before your throne.
Lord, I wanna raise my hands to you,
Lord, I wanna praise the God I serve:

Love you, Lord (love you, Lord).
Almighty King,
love you, Lord (love you, Lord).
You're ev'rything to me.

Lord, I wanna rest, rest in your presence;
Lord, I wanna be filled up once again.
Lord, I wanna stay close to you,
Lord, I wanna say, I love you, Lord:

637 Steve Burnhope

Lord, I want to worship you
the way you want me to,
Lord, I want to find your heart
and be very close to you,
so as I close my eyes and try
to concentrate on you;
touch with your Spirit, Lord,
and fill me through and through.

Lord, I want to worship you, *(x3)*
please help me worship you.

638 Bev Gammon

Lord Jesus, you are faithful,
always with us, never leaving us,
Lord Jesus.

Lord Jesus, you are blameless,
you are perfect, you are sinless,
Lord Jesus.

Lord Jesus, you are so pure,
pure and lovely, pure and holy,
Lord Jesus.

639 James Wright

Lord make me thankful and help me to
    see
all the good things given to me,
for Christmas parties and the carols we
    sing,
for all the laughter and joy that they
    bring.
For all the gifts at this time of year,
that make our Christmas so full of cheer.
The joy of giving as we receive,
from friends and our family.

*And we're freely sharing the goodness
of Christmas with one another,
and we're learning that it's more
blessèd to give than it is to receive.*

640 Iain D. Craig

Lord of the future,
Lord of the past,
Lord of our lives we adore you.
Lord of for ever,
Lord of our hearts,
we give all praise to you.

Lord of tomorrow,
Lord of today,
Lord over all, you are worthy.
Lord of creation,
Lord of all truth,
we give all praise to you.

641 Dave Godfrey

*Lord, our master, wonderful is your
    name.
Oh Lord, our master, wonderful is your
    name.*

Hear your children singing
praises to the King,
enemies are silenced
when the children sing.
And they say . . .

I gaze into the heavens,
when the sunlight fades:
moon and stars are gleaming,
so beautifully made.
And I say . . .

Why are we so special,
you care for everyone.
You've crowned us with the glory
of the risen Son.
And we say . . .

Continued overleaf

*Lord, our master, wonderful is your
    name.
Oh Lord, our master, wonderful is your
    name.*

You've given us control
of animals like sheep:
of birds and fish and creatures
that live within the deep.
And we say . . .

For all your mighty wonders
and ev'rything you do,
we will lift our voices
and sing this song to you.
And we say . . .

642 Unknown

Lord, you know me,
you know ev'rything I do.
You see me when I'm playing
and when I'm working too.
You are all around me
and you take care of me,
even in the night-time
you'll still be close to me.
You know what I'm thinking
and how I feel today.
Help me love you always;
you're A-O-K!

643 Dave Cooke and
          Judy Mackenzie-Dunn

Lord, you see me, Lord, you know me,
you know ev'rything about me:
ev'ry thought inside my head,
ev'ry word before it's said.

Lord, you're with me, all around me
and your hand is here to guide me.
When I sit and when I stand
you are ev'rywhere I am.

*Wherever I go, you are.
Wherever I fly, you're there.
On even the farthest star,
I know you'll find me.
And deep in the darkest night,
you are my sun, my light:
you can make the darkness bright
when you're around me.*

Lord, you made me,
and you love me,
and you're always thinking of me.
It's amazing but it's true,
and you know that I love you.

644 Colin Buchanan

Lots of folk will tell you
that the Bible isn't true.
They'll say it's too old-fashioned,
and that they want something new.
But believing bits of this and that
will never get you through
'cos Jesus is the only way to God.

*Just one truth but lots of lies,
just one way through Jesus Christ,
just one perfect sacrifice,
Jesus is the only way to God.*

When someone makes a new religion
or a new philosophy.
And they'll say what's true is true for you
and this is true for me.
But there's only one Creator
and he's given his decree
that Jesus is the only way to God.

Well, the devil hates the truth
and he is working to deceive.
He cooks up deadly lies
for precious people to believe.
We've got to speak the truth in love
and pray the Lord would make them see
that Jesus is the only way to God.

645 Chris Jackson
based on Mark 12:30

Love the Lord your God
with all your heart, with all your mind.
Love the Lord your God with all your
strength.

Love the Lord with all your heart,
love the Lord with all your strength.

(This song may be sung as a round.)

646 Chris Jackson

Love you, Jesus, I love you, Lord,
I love you more than words can say.
I will follow where you lead,
I will trust you and obey.
So send your Spirit, send your pow'r,
come and fill me, Lord, I pray.
I am waiting for you, Lord,
come and have your way.

647 Colin Buchanan

Woah, woah. (x2)
Made by God for God alone. (x2)

Gotta live your life to the praise of the
  giver
and every breath that fills your lungs.
Gotta live your life to the praise of the
  giver,
the life inside your bones.

Made by God for God alone. (x2)

You've gotta do ev'rything to the praise
  of your maker,
the mighty creator of ev'ryone.
You've gotta do ev'rything to the praise
  of your maker
who holds you together right now.

Made by God for God alone. (x2)
Woah, woah. (x2)

You've gotta come to Jesus to be forgiven,
you ain't livin' 'til the deal is done.
You've gotta come to Jesus to be forgiven,
put your faith in the risen Son.
(Repeat)

Woah, woah. (x2)

648 Philip and Stephanie Chapman

Make a joyful noise to the Lord,
make a joyful noise and sing out loud,
make a joyful noise to the Lord,
sing, sing to the Lord.
Halleluia, halleluia, halleluia, sing out loud.
Halleluia, sing, sing to the Lord.

(Two-part round)

649 John Fryer

Marching in God's army, marching in
  his way.
Marching in God's army all the day.
Shoulders back and head held high,
marching for our King.
He has won the victory,
lift your voice and sing.

By the left, quick march!
We're soldiers of the Lord.
By the right, quick march!
the bible is our sword!
By the left, quick march!
He's won the victory.
By the right, quick march!
and sing this song with me!

650 Philip and Stephanie Chapman

Mary shivers, she's frightened,
she has to go to Bethlehem.
Joseph saddles a donkey,
as they start along the road.
Mary walking, so slowly,
they have a long, long way to go,
Joseph walking beside her.
Who can say what lies ahead?

Mary's child is born (he is born)
and this is the day, this is the day,
this is the day for rejoicing.
This is the day for rejoicing.

Mary watching, Joseph asking,
'Do you have a room to spare?'
Ev'ryone is so busy
and no one seems to care.
Mary crying, there is no room,
so she lies on a bed of straw.
A bright light shines like a diamond,
in a dark and empty sky.

651 Steve Burnhope

Matthew, Mark, Luke and John,
Acts, Romans, one Corinthians,
two Corinthians, Galatians,
Ephesians, Philippians,
Colossians, one and two Thessalonians,
one and two Timothy,
Titus, Philemon, Hebrews,
James, one and two Peter,
one, two and three John,
Jude and Revelation,
these are the books of the New
  Testament,
twenty-seven books and nine authors.

652 Mark and Helen Johnson

Matthew twenty-two, verses thirty-four
  to forty. *(x2)*

One day a Pharisee came to Jesus Christ
and he said, 'Tell me, what's the greatest
  commandment?'
(Repeat)

This is what he said:
Love the Lord your God with all your
  heart,
with all your soul, with all your mind,
with all your strength.
Love the Lord your God with all your
  heart,
with all your soul, with all your mind,
with all your strength.

Love your neighbour as yourself,
and do to others as you'd have them do
  to you.
Love your neighbour as yourself,
and do to others as you'd have them do
  to you.

One day a Pharisee came to Jesus Christ
and he said, 'Tell me, what's the greatest
  commandment?'
(Repeat)

Matthew twenty two, verses thirty four
  to forty. *(x2)*

© 1998 Out of the Ark Music

653 Steve and Kay Morgan-Gurr

May my life be a thank-you
for what you have done,
praising you for your kindness
in sending your Son.
Being filled with your Spirit,
the comforting One,
may my life be a thank-you to you;
may my life be a thank-you to you.

© 1999 Daybreak Music Ltd.

654 Ian Smale and Irene Smale

May my praise be sung with feeling,
may my worship be sincere,
may my voice declare Jesus is God
for all the world to hear.
May my mind be constantly renewed,
may my thoughts be clean and pure,
may my life be dedicated to you,
whom I adore.
I adore you, I adore you;
there's nothing I would rather do
than simply adore you.
I adore you, I adore you;
I want to live my whole life through
simply adoring you.

© 1987 Kingway's Thankyou Music

655 Phil Overton

May the Lord bless you.
May the Lord keep you.
May the Lord make his face
to shine upon you.

May the Lord bless you.
May the Lord be gracious.
May the Lord lift up his countenance
and give you peace.

Hallelujah, hallelujah,
hallelujah, praise his name.

© 2002 Kevin Mayhew Ltd.

656 Graham Kendrick

Meekness and majesty,
manhood and deity,
in perfect harmony,
the Man who is God.
Lord of eternity
dwells in humanity,
kneels in humility
and washes our feet.

  O what a mystery,
  meekness and majesty.
  Bow down and worship
  for this is your God,
  this is your God.

Father's pure radiance,
perfect in innocence,
yet learns obedience
to death on a cross.
Suffering to give us life,
conquering through sacrifice,
and as they crucify
prays: 'Father, forgive.'

Continued overleaf

O what a mystery,
meekness and majesty.
Bow down and worship
for this is your God,
this is your God.

Wisdom unsearchable,
God the invisible,
love indestructible
in frailty appears.
Lord of infinity,
stooping so tenderly,
lifts our humanity
to the heights of his throne.

657 Unknown

Mister Noah built an ark,
the people thought it such a lark.
Mister Noah pleaded so,
but into the ark they would not go.

Down came the rain in torrents,
(splish, splash)
down came the rain in torrents,
(splish, splash)
down came the rain in torrents
and only eight were saved.

The animals went in two by two,
elephant, giraffe and kangaroo.
All were safely stowed away,
on that great and awful day.

Whenever you see a rainbow,
whenever you see a rainbow,
whenever you see a rainbow,
remember that God is love.

658 Andy Read

Monday, Tuesday, Wedn'sday, Thursday,
Friday, Saturday, Sunday, here we go.
Monday, Tuesday, Wedn'sday, Thursday,
Friday, Saturday, Sunday, here we go.
I will praise you ev'ry day,
I will worship, come what may,
there is something deep inside,
I will let it come outside.
Praise you, Lord. Praise you, Lord.

659 Sharon E. Ward

My body is a temple of the Holy Spirit.
My body is a temple of the Holy Spirit.
My body is a temple and Jesus lives
within it.
My body is a temple of the Holy Spirit.
Keep it tidy, keep it clean,
make it sparkle, make it gleam.
My body is a temple of the Holy Spirit.

660 Frank Montgomery and
Bruce Monthy

My God is big enough, my God is big
enough,
my God is big enough for ev'ry
situation.
My God is big enough, my God is big
enough,
my God is big enough for ev'ry situation.

Nowhere I'll ever go, no words I'll ever
say;
nothing that I'll ever do, that you are not
there with me.
I'm in you and you're in me, I'll never
stand alone;
no force that there will ever be can
separate us.

Deeper than the ocean, your word is in
 my heart;
higher than the sky above, your love for
 me is endless.
Stronger than a raging storm, my
 confidence in you;
closer than the air I breathe, you're
 always with me!

© 1998 Christian Faith Center

661 Carole Pegler

My Lord loves me
and oh the wonder I see!
A rainbow shines in my window:
my Lord loves me.

He died for me,
on a cross at Calvary,
he bore my sin and my shame
when he died for me.

© Scripture Union

662 Ian Smale

My mouth was made for worship,
my hands were made to raise,
my feet were made for dancing,
my life is one of praise to Jesus.
And all God's people said: 'Amen,
hallelujah, amen, praise and glory,
amen, amen, amen, amen. Wo, wo, wo, wo.'

My heart was made for loving,
my mind to know God's ways,
my body was made a temple,
my life is one of praise to Jesus.
And all God's people said: 'Amen,
hallelujah, amen, praise and glory,
amen, amen, amen, amen.
Wo, wo, wo, wo, wo.'

© 1989 Glorie Music/Kingsway's Thankyou Music

663 Andy Read

Never ever go, never ever go,
never ever go away from me.
He'll never ever go, never ever go,
never ever go away from me.

Jesus said he would never
ever leave me far behind.
Jesus cares, and he says
nothing I can do will change his mind.

Jesus said he would never
ever stop from loving me.
Jesus cares, and he says
I love you 'cos you're you.
He'll . . .

© 2002 Kevin Mayhew Ltd.

664 John Hardwick

Nobody's a nobody, believe me 'cos it's
 true,
nobody's a nobody, especially not you.
Nobody's a nobody and God wants us
 to see
that ev'rybody's somebody and that
 means even me.

I'm no cartoon, I'm human,
I have feelings, treat me right.
I'm not a superhero
with super strength and might.
I'm not a mega pop star
or super athelete,
but did you know I'm special,
in fact I'm quite unique!

© 1993 Daybreak Music Ltd.

665

John Francis Wade
trans. Frederick Oakeley and others

O come, all ye faithful,
joyful and triumphant,
O come ye, O come ye to Bethlehem;
come and behold him,
born the king of angels:

O come, let us adore him,
O come, let us adore him,
O come, let us adore him,
Christ the Lord.

God of God,
Light of Light,
lo, he abhors not the Virgin's womb;
very God, begotten not created:

See how the shepherds,
summoned to his cradle,
leaving their flocks, draw nigh with lowly
    fear;
we too will thither bend our joyful
    footsteps:

Lo, star-led chieftains,
Magi, Christ adoring,
offer him incense, gold and myrrh;
we to the Christ-child bring our hearts'
    oblations:

Sing, choirs of angels,
sing in exultation,
sing, all ye citizens of heav'n above;
glory to God in the highest:

Yea, Lord, we greet thee,
born this happy morning,
Jesu, to thee be glory giv'n;
Word of the Father, now in flesh
    appearing:

666

Graham Kendrick

O come and join the dance
that all began so long ago,
when Christ the Lord was born in
    Bethlehem.
Through all the years of darkness
still the dance goes on and on,
O, take my hand and come and join the
    song.

Rejoice! (Rejoice!)
Rejoice! (Rejoice!)
O lift your voice and sing,
and open up your heart to welcome
    him.
Rejoice! (Rejoice!)
Rejoice! (Rejoice!)
and welcome now your King,
for Christ the Lord was born in
    Bethlehem.

Come, shed your heavy load
and dance your worries all away,
for Christ the Lord was born in
    Bethlehem.
He came to break the pow'r of sin
and turn your night to day,
O, take my hand and come and join the
    song.

Instrumental verse.

Let laughter ring and angels sing
and joy be all around,
for Christ the Lord was born in
    Bethlehem.
And if you seek with all your heart
he surely can be found,
O, take my hand and come and join the
    song.

667 Steve Burnhope

O God, you're so big,
and I feel so small,
it's really quite amazing
that you notice me at all,
although you live in heaven,
a long, long way away,
you're ev'rywhere on earth as well
and close to me each day.

No wonder, Lord, I worship you,
'cause no-one else is like you,
no wonder, Lord, I worship you
because of who you are,
no wonder I rely on you,
Lord, I'm reaching out to you,
I worship you, I worship you,
I worship you.

There are millions of people
living in this land,
but ev'ry single one of them,
Lord, you understand,
I don't know how you do that,
it's mystery to me,
but I'm just glad that you've got time
for listening to me.

668 Unknown

O happy day! (O happy day!)
O happy day! (O happy day!)
when Jesus washed (when Jesus washed),
when Jesus washed (when Jesus washed),
when Jesus washed (when Jesus washed),
he washed my sins away.
(O happy day!) (O happy day!) O happy
day!
(Repeat)

He taught me how to watch,
watch and pray, watch and pray;
and live rejoicing ev'ry,
ev'ry day, ev'ry day.

669 Sally Wolf

Oh, Lord, send us out with your love
today,
let us carry your light of peace.

Where there is wrong, let us bring your
justice;
where there is hunger, your bread!

Where there is pain, let us bring your
comfort;
where there is sadness, your joy!

670 Paul Crouch and David Mudie

Oh, praise the Lord, sing a brand new
song.
Ev'rybody join in and sing along.
Oh, praise the Lord, sing a brand new
song.
Ev'rybody join in and sing along.

You made us, you love us
and it is plainly obvious
that you cannot restrain your gen'rous
hand.
So you will hold us and keep us,
enfold us in your loving arms
and guide us in the purposes you've
planned.
Oh, praise the Lord.

It's a new song we sing, it's a song for
the King.
He's by our side through thick and thin.
He stooped down low to become our
friend,
and he'll be with us to the end.

671 James Wright

Oh town of Bethlehem
beneath the stars of heav'n,
what is the secret you hold this night?
God's own begotten Son,
heaven's anointed one
has come down.

Come now and behold
the new-born King,
glory of Israel,
come now and behold
the King of all the earth.

Oh what a glorious plan
that brought your love to man;
born in a stable so cold and bare.
From heaven's majesty
to earth's humanity
love came down.

© 2002 Kevin Mayhew Ltd.

672 Phillips Brooks, alt.

O little town of Bethlehem,
how still we see thee lie!
Above thy deep and dreamless sleep
the silent stars go by.
Yet in thy dark streets shineth
the everlasting light;
the hopes and fears of all the years
are met in thee tonight.

O morning stars, together
proclaim the holy birth,
and praises sing to God the King,
and peace upon the earth.
For Christ is born of Mary;
and, gathered all above,
while mortals sleep, the angels keep
their watch of wond'ring love.

How silently, how silently,
the wondrous gift is giv'n!
So God imparts to human hearts
the blessings of his heav'n.
No ear may hear his coming;
but in this world of sin,
where meek souls will receive him, still
the dear Christ enters in.

O holy child of Bethlehem,
descend to us, we pray;
cast out our sin, and enter in,
be born in us today.
We hear the Christmas angels
the great glad tidings tell:
O come to us, abide with us,
our Lord Emmanuel.

673 Patrick Appleford

O Lord, all the world belongs to you,
and you are always making all things new.
What is wrong you forgive,
and the new life you give
is what's turning the world upside down.

The world's only loving to its friends,
but you have brought us love that never
    ends;
loving enemies too,
and this loving with you
is what's turning the world upside down.

This world lives divided and apart.
You draw all men together and we start
in your body to see
that in fellowship, we
can be turning the world upside down.

The world wants the wealth to live in state,
but you show us a new way to be great:
like a servant you came,
and if we do the same,
we'll be turning the world upside down.

O Lord, all the world belongs to you,
and you are always making all things new.
Send your Spirit on all
in your church whom you call
to be turning the world upside down.

674 Jim Bailey

O Lord, I will sing your praise,
O Lord, for the many ways that, Lord,
you have been so good to me.
O Lord, I am saved by grace,
O Lord, what has taken place is more,
so much more than I can say.
Now I am saved to save,
and there's no other way:
salvation's in the name of Jesus.
You came and set me free,
my song will ever be
a song of liberty in Jesus.

675 Jennifer Reay

On a cross he died, he was crucified.
He did it for us, he did it for us.
(Repeat)

But that's not the end of the story;
he was stronger than death.
That's not the end of the story;
for ever he's alive!
He is a tomb breaker, mind shaker;
he is alive!
He is a death beater, life greeter;
he is alive!
(Repeat)

676 Cecil Frances Alexander
(v.4: Michael Forster)

Once in royal David's city
stood a lowly cattle shed,
where a mother laid her baby
in a manger for his bed:
Mary was that mother mild,
Jesus Christ her little child.

He came down to earth from heaven,
who is God and Lord of all,
and his shelter was a stable,
and his cradle was a stall;
with the poor and meek and lowly,
lived on earth our Saviour holy.

And through all his wondrous childhood
day by day like us he grew;
he was little, weak and helpless,
tears and smiles like us he knew;
and he feeleth for our sadness,
and he shareth in our gladness.

Still among the poor and lowly
hope in Christ is brought to birth,
with the promise of salvation
for the nations of the earth;
still in him our life is found
and our hope of heav'n is crowned.

And our eyes at last shall see him
through his own redeeming love,
for that child so dear and gentle
is our Lord in heav'n above;
and he leads his children on
to the place where he is gone.

Not in that poor lowly stable,
with the oxen standing by,
we shall see him, but in heaven,
set at God's right hand on high;
when like stars his children crowned,
all in white shall wait around.

677
Dave Bankhead and Mike Burn
based on Matthew 6:9-13

Our Father in heaven, hallowed be your
    name,
your kingdom come, your will be done
on earth as it is in heaven;
give us today our daily bread,
and forgive us our sins
as we forgive those who sin against us.
Lead us not into temptation,
but deliver us from evil;
for the kingdom, the pow'r and the glory
are yours, now and for ever.
Amen.

678
Paul Field and Stephen Deal

Our Father, who art in heaven,
hallowed be thy name.
Thy kingdom come,
thy will be done
on earth as in heav'n.
Give us today our daily bread
and forgive our sins,
as we forgive each one of those
who sins against us;
and lead us not to the time of trial
but deliver us from evil,
for thine is the kingdom,
the power and the glory.

Let all the people say 'Amen'
in ev'ry tribe and tongue;
let ev'ry heart's desire be joined
to see the kingdom come.
Let ev'ry hope and ev'ry dream be born
in love again;
let all the world sing with one voice,
let the people say 'Amen'.

679
Nick Harding

Our fingers that click come from God,
our fingers that click come from God,
our fingers that click come from God;
ev'rything comes from God.

Our ears that hear . . .

Our feet that stamp . . .

Our head that nods . . .

680
John Lane

Our song's about the greatest man
the world has ever seen.
His life was good in ev'ry way,
not selfish, sly or mean.
The poor folk and the children
all enjoyed his loving care,
now we can know his kindness too,
as if we had been there.

Our song's about the greatest friend,
and Jesus is his name,
he calls us all to follow him,
for that is why he came.
He knows us more than anyone;
he won't forget our names,
though we might change or let him down,
he still remains the same.

Our song's about the King who came
to set his people free.
He healed the sick and cured the deaf,
he helped the blind to see.
His teachings show us how to live
the way we're meant to be.
And when we make this man our King,
it's then we're really free.

Our song's about the one who died,
to show he loves us all.
We feel so weak to do what's right,
we often trip and fall.
But Jesus rose to show his power,
now sin and death can't win,
so he can clear our wrongs away
and help us start again.

Our song's about the Lord who lives,
he's Ruler, Boss and King.
His death is past, this rule will last,
he's King of ev'rything.
His love won't fail, nor strength grow frail,
we always know he's there.
Don't fear what comes, he knows the way,
and we can trust his care.

So Jesus' love can fill our lives
as he has filled our song.
The light of all the world he is,
he shows up all that's wrong.
He gives us hope, forgives our faults
and colours all our days,
we'll open up our lives to him;
we'll give to him our praise.

681 Brenton Brown

Over all the earth, you reign on high,
ev'ry mountain stream, ev'ry sunset sky.
But my one request, Lord, my only aim
is that you'd reign in me again.

Lord, reign in me, reign in your pow'r
over all my dreams, in my darkest hour.
You are the Lord of all I am,
so won't you reign in me again.

Over ev'ry thought, over ev'ry word,
may my life reflect the beauty of my Lord;
'cause you mean more to me than any
    earthly thing,
so won't you reign in me again.

682 Capt. Alan J. Price, CA

O what love, I can hardly believe it;
O what love, I want to receive it;
O what love, I just want to feel it
more and more and more.
(Repeat)

Think of the cost of God's forgiveness,
all that Jesus wants to give us,
through his Spirit's power in us
when, in faith, we turn to him.

Before he made the world,
God chose us to be his
through faith in Jesus.
He will always touch and bless us
when, in faith, we come to him.

683 Kevin Mayhew

Peace, perfect peace,
is the gift of Christ our Lord.
Peace, perfect peace,
is the gift of Christ our Lord.
Thus, says the Lord,
will the world know my friends.
Peace, perfect peace,
is the gift of Christ our Lord.

Love, perfect love . . .

Faith, perfect, faith . . .

Hope, perfect, hope . . .

Joy, perfect, joy . . .

684 Christine Dalton

People can be like a cake –
they decide which one to bake.
Jesus left a recipe
to bake some Christianity.
So, before you cook,
look into his book.

'Cause you don't want to be a
Christian cream puff,
all puffed up and full of air.
No, you don't want to be a doughnut
Christian,
hole in the middle – may be little
but it's not all there!
Or a Christian choc'late crackle
full of noise! Snap, crackle and pop!
I want to be a Christian rock-cake,
full of fruit with God on top.
I'll mix up love, joy, peace, patience,
kindness in a bowl
then add goodness, faithfulness,
gentleness and
stacks of self-control, stacks of self-
control.
That's the Bible's recipe,
Galatians five: twenty-two, twenty-
three.

Christian rock-cakes are the best,
you won't want to be the rest.
God's ingredients you see
make us how we're meant to be.
So, before you cook,
go and get the book.

© 1998 RiverSong Music

685 Dave Godfrey

Praise God, all you people,
praise God, all you nations,
his love for us is strong.
Praise God, all you people,
praise God, all you nations,
his faithfulness goes on
(and on and on and on.)
Psalm one, one, seven is a very short
song!

© 2000 Daybreak Music Ltd.

686 Ian Smale

Praise him, praise him,
bring praises to the Lord our God.
All God's faithful children
must learn to praise him.
(Repeat)

Sing hallelu, hallelu,
sing hallelujah to our God.
All God's faithful children sing
hallelujah, God.

Worship him, worship him,
bring worship to the Lord our God.
All God's faithful children
must learn to worship him.
(Repeat)

© 1982 Kingsway's Thankyou Music

687 Mike Burn

Prayer can make a diff'rence,
prayer can make a diff'rence,
prayer can make a diff'rence, so pray!
(Repeat)

Through prayer our God can heal.
We believe in miracles;
through prayer a whole situation can
   change,
through prayer a person can be born
   again.

Nothing has such power
as a prayer to God my Father.
There's no one else who can do what he
   can,
I want to live my life according to his plan.

688 J. Macpherson

Reach to the Lord, reach out to the Lord.
Reach to the Lord, reach out! Hey!
Reach to the Lord, reach out to the Lord.
Reach to the Lord, reach out! Hey!
Hey, hey, Jesus, it's good to be here,
reaching out to your family.
Hey, hey, Jesus, it's good to be here.
Reach to the Lord, reach out to the
   Lord, reach out! Hey!

Turn to the Lord, turn round to the Lord,
turn to the Lord, turn round! Hey!
Turn to the Lord, turn round to the Lord,
turn to the Lord, turn round! Hey!
Hey, hey, Jesus, it's good to be here,
turning round with your family.
Hey, hey, Jesus, it's good to be here.
Turn to the Lord, turn round to the Lord,
   turn round! Hey!

Jump to the Lord, jump high to the Lord,
jump to the Lord, jump high! Hey!
Jump to the Lord, jump high to the Lord,
jump to the Lord, jump high! Hey!
Jumping high . . .

Shout to the Lord, shout loud to the Lord,
shout to the Lord, shout loud! Hey!
Shout to the Lord, shout loud to the Lord,
shout to the Lord, shout loud! Hey!
Shouting loud . . .

Jump to the Lord, jump high to the
   Lord, jump high! Hey!
Turn to the Lord, turn round to the Lord,
   turn round! Hey!
Reach to the Lord, reach out to the
   Lord, reach out! Hey!

689 Andy Pickford

Reign in me, reign in me
in all of my life, Lord,
won't you reign in me.
(Repeat)

   Closer to you is where I should be.
   So I hear your voice and learn to obey.
   In all that I do, and all that I say,
   Lord, my desire is that you reign in me.

Be with me, be with me
in all of my life, Lord,
won't you be with me.
(Repeat)

690 Chris Jackson

Rejoice! For the Lord is reigning.
Rejoice! For Jesus is King.
Rejoice! For the Lord is reigning,
Jesus is coming and he's coming as King.
Shout and sing to the King of creation,
shout and sing to the Lord who is King.
Lift your voices in jubilation.
Shout and sing to the King.

691 Peter Mangold

Rich man Zac, short as can be,
heard Jesus was coming and he wanted
    to see.
So he climbed right up a sycamore tree,
when Jesus passed that way.

Jesus looked up, said 'Get out of that
    tree,
I want to stay at your place today.'
So Zac climbed down and welcomed
    him in;
when Jesus passed that way.

The people who saw said 'What's he
    done?
He's gone to the house of a wealthy man,
a tax-collector's place to stay.'
When Jesus passed that way.

Zac stood up and said to them all
'I'll give half of my things to the poor,
anyone I've cheated four times I'll pay.'
When Jesus passed that way.

Zac then heard Jesus say,
'Salvation came to this house today.'
He came to seek and he came to save;
when Jesus passed that way,
when Jesus passed that way,
when Jesus passed that way.

© 1996 Peter Mangold. Used by permission

692 Amanda Lofts

Right at the start God made the world,
he made the world, yes, he made the
    world.
Right at the start God made the world,
oh, what a beautiful sight.

On day one, God made night and day,
he made night and day, yes, he made
    night and day.
On day one, God made night and day,
oh, what a beautiful sight.

On day two, God made the sky,
he made the sky, yes, he made the sky.
On day two, God made the sky,
oh, what a beautiful sight.

On day three, God made land and sea,
he made plants and trees, he made land
    and sea.
On day three, God made plants and trees,
oh, what a beautiful sight.

On day four, God made sun, moon and
    stars,
sun, moon and stars, sun, moon and
    stars.
On day four, God made sun, moon and
    stars,
oh, what a beautiful sight.

On day five, God made fish and the birds,
fish and the birds, yes, fish and the birds.
On day five, God made fish and the birds,
oh, what a beautiful sight.

On day six, God made animals and us,
animals and us, yes, animals and us.
On day six, God made animals and us,
oh, what a beautiful sight.

On day seven, God had a rest,
God had a rest, God had a rest.
On day seven, God had a rest,
thank you for making the world.

© 2001 Sovereign Lifestyle Music

693

Andy Read

Save me, Lord, save me Lord,
save me, Lord in Jesus' name.
Save me, Lord, save me, Lord,
save me, Lord, in Jesus' name.
He came to me when I was down,
he came to me when I was out,
he came to me in my sin,
he came to me and set me free!

694

Laura Wright and Chris Laughlin

Say amen to the Lord for he has
conquered.
Say amen to the Lord today.
Say amen to the Lord for he has
conquered.
Oh hip, hip, hip hooray.

See the devil falling down on his knees,
hear him begging, 'Jesus, please, please,
please.'
How he'd love to claim this victory,
but the battle belongs to the Lord,
yes, the battle belongs to the Lord.

'Make way for the King of kings',
say the angels on high.
We see him coming down from out of
the sky.
He has come to save us all.
Thank you, Jesus, Lord, my Saviour.
Thank you, Jesus, Lord, my Saviour.

This coda is sung after a chorus and
before the final chorus:

Our prayers have not been in vain
so we will sing it again.

695

Edward Caswall

See, amid the winter's snow,
born for us on earth below,
see, the Lamb of God appears,
promised from eternal years.

Hail, thou ever-blessèd morn!
Hail, redemption's happy dawn!
Sing through all Jerusalem:
Christ is born in Bethlehem!

Lo, within a manger lies,
he who built the starry skies,
he who, throned in height sublime,
sits amid the cherubim.

Say, ye holy shepherds, say,
what your joyful news today;
wherefore have you left your sheep
on the lonely mountain steep?

'As we watched at dead of night,
lo, we saw a wondrous light;
angels, singing peace on earth,
told us of the Saviour's birth.'

Sacred infant, all divine,
what a tender love was thine,
thus to come from highest bliss,
down to such a world as this!

Teach, O teach us, holy child,
by thy face so meek and mild,
teach us to resemble thee
in thy sweet humility.

696

Roger Jones – from
While Shepherds Watched (1987)

Sheep! Sheep! Is there anything more
to life than sheep?
Sheep! Sheep! Is there anything more
than sheep?

Continued overleaf

We work all day for not much pay,
to barely earn our keep!
In bed at night, can you guess our
    plight?
(Yawn) I can't sleep!
We end up counting sheep!

*Sheep! Sheep! Is there anything more
    to life than sheep?
Sheep! Sheep! Is there anything more
    than sheep?*

King David was a shepherd-boy,
at night he used to keep
his watchful eye on his flocks, but why?
Someone please tell me why
should anyone want his sheep!

We go to town, but people frown
as 'round the streets we creep.
'Not welcome here! Out of town, d'you
    hear!
In the fields, that your place!
Go back to keep your sheep!'

Oompah, oompah! There's a woolly
    jumpah!
No, it's just a lamb!
What can it be? Is it plain to see?
Is it him? Is it her? Is it you or me?
No, it's just a ewe or ram!

697 Joseph Mohr
trans. John Freeman Young

Silent night, holy night.
All is calm, all is bright,
round yon virgin mother and child;
holy infant, so tender and mild,
sleep in heavenly peace,
sleep in heavenly peace.

Silent night, holy night.
Shepherds quake at the sight,
glories stream from heaven afar,
heav'nly hosts sing alleluia:
Christ the Saviour is born,
Christ the Saviour is born.

Silent night, holy night.
Son of God, love's pure light,
radiant beams from thy holy face,
with the dawn of redeeming grace:
Jesus, Lord, at thy birth,
Jesus, Lord, at thy birth.

trans. John Freeman Young

698 Dave Cooke and Paul Field

Sing a new song to the Lord, all around
    the world.
Sing a new song to the Lord, all around
    the world.
All the praise that we can bring, will
    never be enough.
Tell somebody ev'ry day the wonder of
    his love.

*And we'll sing glory, glory, glory to his
    name.
Let the beauty of his holiness set our
    hearts aflame.
Let the heavens be glad, let the earth
    rejoice and sing:
we'll sing glory, glory, glory to the
    King.*

Sing a new song to the Lord, all around
    the earth.
Sing a new song to the Lord, all around
    the earth.
He is wise and he is strong, on him we
    can depend.
Tell somebody ev'ry day his kingdom
    never ends.

699 Gill Hutchinson

Sing a song to the Lord, be joyful and
sing,
let his praise be heard in ev'ry nation,
wonderful and mighty is his name.
Shout the praise of the Lord, let
everyone hear,
there is none like him in all creation.
Worship him for ever. He's the same.
Come and praise him, for he is the King
of glory
and he reigns on earth below, in heaven
above.
Come and praise him, he is worthy of
our worship
and he gives us all his everlasting love.

© 1997 Sea Dream Music

700 Ian Smale

Sing hallelujah, hallelujah,
praise the Lord, praise the Lord.
Hallelujah, praise the Lord.
Sing hallelujah, hallelujah,
praise the Lord, praise the Lord.
Hallelujah, praise the Lord.
Praise the Lord, hallelujah,
hallelujah, praise the Lord.
Hallelujah, praise the Lord.
Hallelujah, praise the Lord.
Hallelujah, praise the Lord.
Hallelujah, praise the Lord.
(Repeat)

© 1998 Glorie Music/Kingsway's Thankyou Music

701 Mark and Helen Johnson

Sing out an Easter song,
tell ev'ryone that the Lord has risen,
sing out a joyful song,
tell ev'rybody that he's alive!

Jesus Christ, Son of God,
gave his life upon a cross,
but the pow'r of death was not
enough to hold him down.

Taken down from public view,
he was placed inside a tomb,
but the pow'r of love broke through
and raised him back to life.

He returned to see his friends,
showed himself alive again.
What a day it must have been
to have him back again!

© 1991 Out of the Ark Music

702 J. Macpherson

Slap a hand and pat a back and wink an
eye;
you'll spread good cheer.
Walk a mile and share a smile and talk it
over;
all comes clear.
Look and see and try to be a friend
who lends a list'ning ear.
Walk and talk together.
Maybe we could live in peace.

© J. Macpherson
Used by permission

703 James Wright

Sleep, holy child, born on this night,
angels and mortals bow down
at this holy sight.
Who would have thought
one born so small
would grow from a child to a King
and become Saviour of all.

Continued overleaf

Glory to God, give glory to God,
with the host of heaven we sing,
we bow down and worship
the new-born King.
Glory to God, give glory to God,
with the host of heaven we sing,
we bow down and worship
the new-born King.
Bow down and worship
Jesus the King.
Bow down and worship
Jesus the King.

Two thousand years have passed and
    gone
yet we remember the night
your glory shone.
Nations may rise,
kingdoms may fall,
yet the light of heaven shines on
Jesus, the Saviour of all.

704 Tim Moyler and Ichthus Beckenham children

Some days are not easy, some days are
    tough,
sometimes people hurt you and you've
    just had enough.
Where have all your friends gone,
who can you find to listen to the worries
    that spin round in your mind?
Tell me what shall I do, who can I trust?
Who will be with me and won't let me
    down?

Trust in the Lord your God when the
*   sun rises,*
trust in him when the sun sets,
keep trusting even when you feel he's
*   not with you,*
'cos he's always near you, he promises.
He's always near you, he promises.

705 Phil Chapman and Sharon Waspe

Sometimes I can't understand and I
    struggle to see
God's will and God's plan working round
    about me.
And yet he still calls me with all of my sin
to show other people their way back to
    him.

I often am troubled and wrestle with sin.
My words and my actions, my thoughts
    deep within.
Lord, give me discernment and grant me
    your peace
and my vision of Christ as my Saviour
    increase.

My Saviour, my comfort, he knows me
    throughout.
He gives me his promise and why
    should I doubt?
My rock and my shelter, my guide and
    my friend,
he loves the unlovely: on him I'll depend.

In mercy my Father, look down from
    above
for in word and in action I hurt those I
    love.
I come in repentance and ask that your
    grace
be extended still further to me in these
    days.

To know you more fully, reveal to me
yourself in your glory one God who is
    three.
My Father, my comforter, my Saviour, my
    Lord
who one day I'll worship as I truly
    should.

706 Christine Dalton

Sometimes life is an uphill climb,
Devil loves working overtime.
He laughs when I do things wrong,
my will-pow'r is not that strong.
Sometimes life is a downhill slide,
Devil gives me a rocky ride.
How he loves to torment me,
Hercules, please rescue me.
Batman and Robin, where are you?
I need your muscles to pull me through!
What good are heroes on TV?
They never come to rescue me!

Power Rangers and Superman
never bother the Devil's plan.
This is a battle they can't fight
between the pow'rs of dark and light.
Bible stories often tell
about a man who conquered Hell.
Jesus fought in his Father's name
and beat the Devil at his own game.
Jesus, you're my champion!
Heaven's hero, God the Son.
I don't need muscles and I don't need
    swords;
just say 'Jesus Christ is Lord.'

707 Phil Chapman

Sov'reign Lord, to you we sing;
hymns of praise to you we bring.
For your goodness true and pure
seed-time and harvest shall endure.

Rain and sun and crops preserved,
gifts to us so undeserved.
Help us better to recall
God of love who gives us all.

Food a-plenty by your might,
choice so varied for our delight!
For your gifts let praise be giv'n,
ev'ry meal a gift from heav'n.

708 Steve and Kay Morgan-Gurr

*Step out with Jesus, walk away from
    trouble,
follow him closely for the road is long.
If he leads slowly, or at the double;
stay close beside him and you won't
    go wrong.*

You need to travel with important things
    with you;
a map, a guide, a lamp for when it's
    night.
We have the Bible, and we have the
    Spirit too,
and close to Jesus he will be our light,
    light, light.

You have to watch your step
as you walk through each day.
It's often hard to go against the flow.
Don't follow all the people on the easy
    way,
just follow Jesus, he's the way to go, go,
    go.

709 Alex Legg

Sun-deedle, sun-deedle, my day of rest,
Sunday's the one day that I love the
    best.
When God made the world, he saw it
    was blessed,
then he rested on Sun-deedle day.

Continued overleaf

He coloured the sky and he painted the
    world,
he made all the boys and he made little
    girls,
out of straight lines and circles and
    squiggles and curls.
Then he rested on Sun-deedle day.

710   Nick Harding

Take the Bible, live it out,
listen and learn, jump and shout.
Come together, start today,
if you want to really live God's way.

Worship God and nothing more,
that's what he designed us for!
Think of God in all you say,
if you want to really live God's way.

711   Iain D. Craig

Teach me to trust you, Lord Jesus,
help me to draw close to you.
Let me be filled with your love and delight,
Lord may I know more of you.

Teach me to pray to you, Jesus,
please give me the right words to say.
Help me to pray for my friends at school,
so they may get to know you.

Teach me to love you, Lord Jesus,
show me the things I must do.
Help me to get to that place, O Lord,
where I can be close to you.

712   Mark and Helen Johnson

Tell me who made all of creation,
who designed the wonders of nature?
Whose idea was pattern and colour,
wonderful to see?

Everywhere around me,
I can see the hand of God,
the evidence surrounds me,
in the greatness of his world.

Tell me who made music and laughter,
who designed our bodies to start with?
Whose idea was thinking and feeling,
who gave life to me?

Don't stop looking, don't stop believing,
God is to be found when you seek him.
All creation tells of his glory for eternity.

713   Martin Smith

Thank you for saving me; what can I say?
You are my ev'rything, I will sing your
    praise.
You shed your blood for me; what can I
    say?
You took my sin and shame, a sinner
    called by name.

Great is the Lord.
Great is the Lord.
For we know your truth has set us
    free;
you've set your hope in me.
(Last time: *Thank you for saving me;*
    what can I say?)

Mercy and grace are mine, forgiv'n is my
  sin;
Jesus, my only hope, the Saviour of the
  world.
'Great is the Lord,' we cry; God, let your
  kingdom come.
Your word has let me see, thank you for
  saving me.

714 Kate Abba

Thank you, God, for this good day
and keep me safe in you, I pray.
That you should keep me in your care
is my hope, my joy, my life, my prayer.

> *When I consider the heavens and all*
>   *you have made,*
> *the sun and the moon and the light*
>   *and the shade,*
> *the mountains and rivers and stars up*
>   *above,*
> *yet you gave yourself to me in love.*

Keep me warm throughout the night,
enfold me in your shining light.
You raised me more than is my due
and give me honour, glory too.

Take my hand and show me the way,
take my heart and love me, I pray.
Show me a love, one like I've never known,
for your love will take me away.

715 Andrew and Pauline Pearson

Thank you, Lord, for the bright blue sky.
Thank you, Lord, for the birds that fly.
Thank you, Lord, for the mountains so
  high.
Thank you, Lord, for your beautiful
  world.

Thank you, Lord, thank you, Lord.
Thank you, Lord, for your beautiful
  world.

Thank you, Lord, for the very blue sea.
Thank you, Lord, for the very tall tree.
Thank you, Lord, for making me 'me'.
Thank you, Lord, for your beautiful
  world.

716 Ian Smale

The birds can fly and the monkeys swing.
The fat worm wiggles and the bee can
  sting.
The lion roars whilst the wise owl thinks.
The fox can run and the skunk just
  stinks.
But, Lord, I am not like all these,
I'm a little child just keen to please.
What can I do? What can I be?
Jesus says just be like me.

717 Andrew and Pauline Pearson

The fingers of my hand help me to
  understand
that Jesus loves me very much, very
  much.
(Repeat)

All the hairs on our heads are counted.
All the names we are called are
  recorded.
All the things we do wrong are forgotten
because Jesus loves me very much, very
  much.

718

from William Sandys' 'Christmas Carols, Ancient and Modern,' alt.

The first Nowell the angel did say
was to certain poor shepherds in fields
  as they lay:
in fields where they lay keeping their
  sheep,
on a cold winter's night that was so deep.

Nowell, Nowell, Nowell, Nowell,
born is the King of Israel!

They lookèd up and saw a star,
shining in the east, beyond them far,
and to the earth it gave great light,
and so it continued both day and night.

And by the light of that same star,
three wise men came from country far;
to seek for a king was their intent,
and to follow the star wherever it went.

This star drew nigh to the north-west,
o'er Bethlehem it took its rest,
and there it did both stop and stay
right over the place where Jesus lay.

Then entered in those wise men three,
full rev'rently upon their knee,
and offered there in his presence,
their gold and myrrh and frankincense.

Then let us all with one accord
sing praises to our heav'nly Lord,
who with the Father we adore
and Spirit blest for evermore.

719 Chris Jackson

The fruit of the Spirit is love, joy, peace,
patience, kindness, and goodness too;
gentleness and faithfulness and self-
  control.
That's what the Spirit will grow in you,
  oh, oh!

When you're tired of helping out
you just want to scream and shout,
and you feel that selfish old nature rise
  up in you.
Just remember!

The Spirit will give you the pow'r,
the Spirit will give you the strength.
He's the one who will help you stand up
and fight the selfish nature!

© 2000 Powerpack/Learning Curve Music

720 Susanna Levell
based on Galatians 5:22

The fruit of the Spirit is love, joy and
  peace,
patience and kindness and goodness to
  all,
faithfulness, gentleness, self-control,
live by the Spirit of God.

© 2002 Kevin Mayhew Ltd.

721 Ian Smale

The going is hard and the going is tough.
I'm feeling exhausted, I'm feeling rough.
But I'm staying with Jesus till the end of
  the line.
'Cause not long from now it will be
  party-time.
Hey, yip-pee-yi-yea, hey, yip-pee-yi-yo.
There's no looking back, I'm gonna go
  go go.
Hey, yip-pee-yi-yo, hey, yip-pee-yi-yea.
When Jesus returns we will party all day!

© 1998 Glorie Music. Administered by Kingsway's Thankyou Music

722 Steve Burnhope

The Holy Spirit is a 'he', not an 'it' *(not an 'it')!*
The Holy Spirit is a 'he', not an 'it' *(not an 'it')!*
The Holy Spirit is a 'he', how would you feel if you were he
and ev'rybody in the church called you 'it' *(called you 'it')?*

723 Ian Smale

The Lord loves me, he really, really loves me.
The Lord loves me, I want you all to know. Hey!
The Lord loves me, he really, really loves me:
I am his and he is mine, the Bible tells me so.

724 Dave Godfrey

The nations around Israel had gods of wood and stone,
the prophet Jeremiah said: 'Don't make those gods your own.'
Precious silver, human hands, what good can idols do?
And when it comes to lasting things, this scripture is true!

They're like a scarecrow in a melon patch!
Can't walk, can't talk, can't do, can't do anything that's lasting,
like a scarecrow in a melon patch.

And the people in the world today make gods of many things,
though idols remain powerless to forgive all man's sins.
Football players, top pop stars, are good at what they do.
But when it comes to lasting things, this scripture is true!

Like Jeremiah long ago, I'll gently bow the knee,
to the God who made the universe and give his life for me.
Mighty Saviour, Jesus Christ, you're good at all you do.
And when it comes to lasting things, I will trust in you.

'Cos you're the King of all eternity!
You walk, and talk, you do, you do ev'rything that's lasting,
you're the King of all eternity.

I'll worship you, worship you, worship you, you're the King of all eternity.
(Repeat)

(To end song)
You walk, and talk, you do,
you do ev'rything that's lasting,
you're the King of all eternity.

725 Cecil Frances Alexander

There is a green hill far away,
outside a city wall,
where the dear Lord was crucified,
who died to save us all.

We may not know, we cannot tell,
what pains he had to bear,
but we believe it was for us
he hung and suffered there.

Continued overleaf

He died that we might be forgiv'n,
he died to make us good;
that we might go at last to heav'n,
saved by his precious blood.

There was no other good enough
to pay the price of sin;
he only could unlock the gate
of heav'n, and let us in.

O dearly, dearly has he loved,
and we must love him too,
and trust in his redeeming blood,
and try his works to do.

726 Charles Kirby

There is (clap) no mountain high
enough (clap, clap)
no river wide enough. (clap, clap)
No ocean deep enough to hide me
from God's love.
There is (clap) no mountain high
enough (clap, clap)
no river wide enough. (clap, clap)
No ocean deep enough to hide me
from God's love. (clap, clap, clap)

No desert dry enough, no jungle thick
enough,
no darkness black enough to hide me
from God's love.

There is (clap) no mountain high
enough (clap, clap)
no river wide enough. (clap, clap)
No ocean deep enough to hide me
from God's love. (clap, clap, clap)

No king is great enough, no army large
enough,
no power strong enough to hide me
from God's love.

No sin is bad enough, no troubles tough
enough,
no questions hard enough to hide me
from God's love.

© 1976 Hope Publishing Co./Copycare

727 Sammy Horner

There is one who is for us, no matter
who's against us,
there is one, only one, and I trust his
ev'ry word.
And there is one who is for us, no
matter who's against us.
There is one, only one, the blessèd,
risen Son.
There is one and his name is Christ
the Lord.

When my spirit tires within me
it's only you who knows my way.
If men have hidden traps to snare me
I'll call your name and to my enemies I say:

I cry to you, you are my refuge.
You listen to me when I need
you set me free from my prison,
and that is why I praise your name,
you're great indeed.

© 1999 Daybreak Music Ltd.

728 Philip and Stephanie Chapman

There I was, walking with my wellyboots,
splosh, splosh, splosh through the mud.
And as I was squelching along,
I heard a blackbird singing a song:
(whistle)

On the ground, in a tree,
through the air or under the sea,
I know whoever we may be,
God loves you and God loves me.

There I was, walking with my wellyboots,
splosh, splosh, splosh through the mud.
And as I was squelching along,
I heard a cow singing a song: *(moo)*

*Add extra verses as required

So think about the ones you love
and all that you can do
to help them feel all your love so real,
just as Jesus loves you too.

729 Chris Jackson and Jill Hoffmann

There's a river flowing,
and a wind that's blowing,
there's a fire burning in our hearts.
Our love for you is growing,
more of Jesus knowing,
Father send your Spirit from above.
Oh, come river of love,
fill me again power of God,
over and over again,
over and over again,
over and over again.

730 Philip and Stephanie Chapman

There's a special feeling in the air,
it's Christmas time again,
when from heav'n above God sent his love
when his Son Jesus came.

*There are lots of presents to give
    each other
that don't need money at all,
when we show our love, when they
    know we care,
that's the best gift we can share.*

Remember all that Jesus brings
each day the whole year through,
he gives us help and he gives us love
and he gave his life for you.

731 James Wright

*There's a star that shines so bright
on this still and holy night.
Heaven's own begotten Son
is born this happy morn.
There's a joy that fills the air,
it's a joy that all can share.
For the Saviour of the world
is born this happy morn.*

Shepherds in the fields are dazzled
by a glorious sight,
angels singing glory to the Saviour born
this happy morning.

Wisemen travel far to gaze
and worship at his feet,
bearing precious gifts before the Saviour
born this happy morning.

732 Steve and Kay Morgan-Gurr

There's nothing, nothing I can do or say
to make God love me more.
He fathers me in such a way
it lasts for evermore.
The Bible says that it's called grace,
I see it there in Jesus' face:
there's nothing, nothing I can do or say
to make God love me more,
to make God love me more.

Continued overleaf

There's nothing, nothing I can do or say
to make God love me less.
I need forgiveness ev'ry day,
and Jesus' righteousness.
But when I turn to him and pray
he gives his mercy right away:
there's nothing I can do or say
to make God love me less,
to make God love me less.

733   Amanda Lofts

There was a clever man who had a
    clever plan
to build a lovely house all safe and strong.
He found a nice firm rock
and went knock, knock, knock.
He'd built a lovely house before too long.

And the lightning flashed and the
    thunder crashed,
and the wind was blowing and the
    snow was snowing.
The rain poured down, the man was
    safe and sound.
His house was safe and strong. His
    house was safe and strong.

There was a silly man who had a silly plan
to build a house as quickly as he could.
He found some sand so flat and went
    splat, splat, splat.
The silly man thought it looked quite
    good.

And the lightning flashed and the
    thunder crashed,
and the wind was blowing and the
    snow was snowing.
The rain went splash and his house
    went crash!
His house was washed away. His
    house was washed away.

Be like the clever man, and have a clever
    plan
to listen to the things that God tells you.
So go and find his book and look, look,
    look
and do the things he's telling you to do.

And the lightning flashed and the
    thunder crashed,
and the wind was blowing and the
    snow was snowing.
The rain poured down, the man was
    safe and sound.
His house was safe and strong. His
    house was safe and strong.

734   Robin Mark

These are the days of Elijah,
declaring the word of the Lord;
and these are the days of your servant,
    Moses,
righteousness being restored.
And though these are days of great trial,
of famine and darkness and sword,
still we are the voice in the desert crying,
'Prepare ye the way of the Lord.'

Behold, he comes riding on the clouds,
shining like the sun at the trumpet call;
lift your voice, it's the year of jubilee,
out of Zion's hill salvation comes.

These are the days of Ezekiel,
the dry bones becoming as flesh;
and these are the days of your servant,
    David,
rebuilding a temple of praise.
These are the days of the harvest,
the fields are as white in the world,
and we are the lab'rers in your vineyard,
declaring the word of the Lord.

735 Capt Alan J. Price, CA

These are the things we believe that
  are true;
God has revealed them to me and to
  you.

God, our creator, our Father above,
sent his Son, Jesus, to show his great love.

Jesus was killed, though no wrong he
  had done;
part of God's plan to forgive ev'ryone.

Risen from death, then to heaven he
  went,
and just as he promised, the helper he
  sent.

Spirit, our helper, works in you and me,
'til Jesus returns and with him we will be.

These are the things we believe that
  are true;
things God has given for me and for
  you.

736 Chris Jackson
based on Isaiah 40:31

They that hope in the Lord shall renew
  their strength,
they that hope in the Lord shall renew
  their strength.
They will soar up with wings like eagles,
they will run and not grow weary,
they will walk, and not faint.
They will soar up with wings like eagles,
they will run and not grow weary,
they will walk, and not faint.

737 Graham Kendrick

This Child, secretly comes in the night,
O this Child, hiding a heavenly light,
O this Child, coming to us like a stranger,
this heavenly Child.

This Child, heaven come down
now to be with us here,
heavenly love and mercy appear,
softly in awe and wonder come near –
to this heavenly Child.

This Child, rising on us like the sun,
O this Child, given to light everyone,
O this Child, guiding our feet on the
  pathway
to peace on earth.

This Child, raising the humble and poor,
O this Child, making the proud ones to
  fall;
O this Child, filling the hungry with good
  things,
this heavenly Child.

738 Andrew and Pauline Pearson

This is a noisy song,
a noisy song to Jesus.
This is a noisy song,
that I can sing to him.

This is a clapping song . . .

This is a marching song . . .

This is a quiet song . . .

This is a noisy song . . .

739

John Hardwick
based on Isaiah 40:31

Those who put their hope in the Lord,
those who put their hope in the Lord,
those who put their hope in the Lord
will renew their strength.
(Repeat)

They will soar on wings like eagles,
they will run and not be weary,
they will walk and not be faint.
(Repeat)

740

Iain D. Craig

Though I am little, though I am small,
Lord, I can trust you in all things.
You always stay close by my side,
Lord, I can trust you in all things.

You never leave me, I'm never alone.
When I sit at your feet I am close to your
    throne.
You always love me and care for my needs.
Lord, I can trust you in all things.

741

Ian Smale

Three, nine, thirty-nine,
thirty-nine books are in the Old
    Testament.
Two, seven, twenty-sev'n,
but there's only twenty-seven in the New.

*But just one holy God
could bring the book to life
and promise ev'ry word is true.
The one and only living God
told the writers what they should and
    shouldn't do.*

Two, eight, twenty-eight,
over twenty-eight authors in the Old
    Testament,
but just nine, only nine,
there are only nine authors in the New.

Two, comma, nought, nought, nought,
two thousand years are covered in the
    Old Testament,
but even less than one, nought, nought,
less than one hundred years are covered
    in the New.

742

J. Macpherson

Tick tock goes the clock,
tick tock, tick tock.
Drip-a-drip goes the tap,
drip-a-drip, drip-a-drip.
Croak, croak goes the frog,
croak, croak, croak, croak.
That's the sound of the night.

Brr, brr goes the phone,
brrr, brrr, brrr, brrr.
Ding dong goes the door,
ding dong, ding dong.
Clatter, clatter go the plates,
clatter, clatter, clatter, clatter.
That's the sound of the house.

*Let ev'rything
that makes a sound
give praise to God.
Let the earth resound.
Let ev'rything that lives and breathes
give praise to God on the land and sea.*

Woo, woo goes the horn,
woo, woo, woo, woo.
'All aboard', goes the guard,
'all aboard, all aboard'.
Clacketty clack go the wheels,
clacketty clack, clacketty clack.
That's the sound of the train.
Breep, breep goes the ref,
breep, breep, breep, breep.
Boing, boing goes the ball,
boing, boing, boing, boing.
Hip hooray goes the crowd,
hip hooray, hip hooray.
That's the sound of the game.

Let ev'rything
that makes a sound
give praise to God.
Let the earth resound.
Let ev'rything that lives and breathes
give praise to God on the land and sea.

Boom, boom goes the bass,
boom, boom, boom, boom.
Rat-a-tat goes the drum,
rat-a-tat, rat-a-tat.
Tweedle dee goes the fife,
tweedle dee, tweedle dee.
That's the sound of the band.

Wark, wark goes the crow,
wark, wark, wark, wark.
Moo, moo goes the cow,
moo, moo, moo, moo.
Oink, oink goes the pig,
oink, oink, oink, oink.
That's the sound of the farm.

Let ev'rything
that makes a sound
give praise to God.
Let the earth resound.
Let ev'rything that lives and breathes
give praise to God on the land and sea.

743   Capt. Alan J. Price, CA

Tick, tock, tick, tock,
life is rather like a clock;
I am like a little wheel,
however big or small I feel;
God can use in his plan,
I can serve him as I am;
isn't it good? Isn't it good?

744   Doug Horley

Touch a finger, touch a thumb,
touch a wrist, touch an elbow,
touch a shoulder, touch a head,
ev'ry bit of you is special.
Touch a finger, touch a thumb,
touch a wrist, touch an elbow,
touch a shoulder, touch an ear,
ev'ry bit of you is special.

If you're short and fat,
or tall and thin,
got knobbly knees or
fifteen chins;
doesn't matter just what shape you're in,
God loves you as you are.

Touch a finger, touch a thumb,
touch a wrist, touch an elbow,
touch a shoulder, touch an eyebrow,
ev'ry bit of you is special.
Touch a toe, touch an ankle,
touch a knee, touch a hip,
touch a back, bump a bottom,
touch a nose; touch lips!

745 Andy Read

Turn to the Lord, turn to the Lord,
turn to the Lord and praise him.
Turn to the Lord, turn to the Lord,
turn to the Lord and praise him.
(Repeat)

For he is good, for he is kind,
he has power to deliver me.
He is holy, full of mercy,
he has power to deliver me.

From my fear, from my sin,
he has power to deliver me.
He is love, he is light,
power to deliver me.

Turn to the Lord, turn to the Lord,
turn to the Lord and praise him.
Turn to the Lord, turn to the Lord,
turn to the Lord and praise him.
(Repeat)

Praise him! Praise him!
Power to deliver me.
Bop bop boo-wop,
bop bop boo-wop,
bop bop boo-wop,
bop bop bop bop bop.

(*Last time:* Praise him! Praise him!
Power to deliver me.)

746 Mark and Helen Johnson

Unto us a child is born,
unto us a Son is given.
He shall reign in all the earth,
he will be called Emmanuel!
(Repeat)

Angel voices sing,
hallelujahs ring,
for today in Bethlehem
the love of God has come to men,
the Saviour of the world
is Christ the King!

Leave your cares aside,
seek and you will find,
for today in Bethlehem
the love of God has come to men,
the Saviour of the world
is Jesus Christ!

Come, let us adore,
now and evermore,
for today in Bethlehem
the love of God has come to men,
the Saviour of the world
is Christ the Lord!

747 John Hardwick

We are a new generation in a new
    millennium,
wanting to do what is right.
We are a new generation in a new
    millennium,
walking in God's light.
We are a new generation in a new
    millennium,
not know what the future holds.
We are a new generation in a new
    millennium,
putting our hope in the Lord.
(Repeat)

Some put their hope in riches,
some put their hope in fame.
Some put their hope in good looks;
but that seems such a shame.
I'm putting my hope in the one thing
that has a guarantee.
I'm putting my hope in Jesus;
he is the one for me!

He's the same yesterday, today and for
    ever
and his love lasts eternally.
He's the same yesterday, today and for
    ever
and his love lasts eternally.

748 Dave Bankhead and Mike Burn

We are God's chosen, holy nation,
we belong to him alone
and may this rising generation
worship Christ upon his throne,
worship Christ upon his throne.

We believe in God the Father,
and in Christ, his precious Son.
We believe he died to save us,
came to call us as his own.

We believe he sends his Spirit
on us now with gifts of power.
Hear the Spirit calling out to us,
where he leads us we will go.

749 Capt. Alan J. Price, CA

We are here, waiting,
we are here, seeking,
we are here, knowing
the love of God.

We are here, needing,
we are here, asking,
we are here, wanting
a touch from God.

The touch of his Son, Jesus Christ,
the touch of his Spirit, Lord of life:
the touch of our God to make us all
that he wants us to be.
(Repeat)

We are here, waiting,
we are here, seeking,
we are here, knowing
you love us, Lord.
We are here, needing,
we are here, asking,
we are here, wanting
a touch from you,
wanting a touch from you,
wanting a touch from you.

750 Margaret Carpenter

We are in the army, the army of the Lord,
fighting all our battles with the power of
    God's word.

We are in the army, the army of the
    Lord,
fighting all our battles with the power
    of God's word.
Helmet of salvation, sword of the
    Spirit high,
the shield of faith protecting us from
    the devil's ugly lies.

Devil, you're a liar and we know all your
    tricks.
We are not deceived by you, 'cos Jesus'
    got you licked.

751 Ian Smale

We are marching along in the pow'r of
    God,
with our armour on, we are fit and strong.
We are marching along in the pow'r of
    God,
we are soldiers, little soldiers of the King.

752 Doug Horley

We are warriors, gonna fight
and we're gonna pray;
we are warriors, gonna fight
and we're gonna pray, yeah.

Kicking down the strongholds
of the enemies of God,
we are gonna see miracles:
crying to our King,
pleading for this nation
we declare we're gonna break through.

   'Cause . . .

753 Terry Tarsiuk

We can heal our world,
we can show the love of Jesus.
We can heal our world,
we can say he truly frees us.
We can heal our world,
we can love them through their sorrow.
We can heal our world,
we can give a bright tomorrow.

Lost, blinded by what they believe in,
losing their sight;
lost, stumbling alone in the darkness
in search of the light;
you, only you can really ever satisfy,
you, only you are the answer to their
   hurting cry!

Hearts as dry as the sunburned desert,
in need of the rain;
hearts so bruised by the blows of
   indiff'rence
they feel so much pain;
you, only you can really ever satisfy,
you, only you are the answer to their
   hurting cry!

754 Chris Wyman and Tony Cooke

We dance to praise the Lord!
We dance to bless his name!
We dance to praise the name of Jesus!
We dance to praise you, Lord!
We dance to bless your name!
We dance to praise your name,
   Lord Jesus!
Lift your hands into the air!
Make a joyful noise and dance before
   the Lord!

755 Andrew and Wendy Rayner

We have a mega-story,
a headline for the world,
that Jesus loves and cares for us,
for ev'ry boy and girl.
So we'll broadcast all about it
with action, light and sound.
We need to tell ev'ryone
the best news has been found.

   Good news, Jesus loves you.
   We'll shout it loud and clear.
   Good news, Jesus loves you,
   it's the best news you can hear.

Optional Christmas verse:
Now love came down at Christmas,
for God loves ev'ryone.
'Cause we all need forgiveness,
he gave his only Son.
So come on, ev'rybody,
let's worship him and sing.
We need to tell ev'ryone
that Jesus is the King.

756 Terry Tarsuik

We have been called a chosen
 generation,
a royal priesthood, a holy nation.
We have been called his own special
 people;
we will proclaim the praises of his
 marvellous light.

Lord, my life is a song
since you came along
and now I belong to you only.
Lord, how awesome you are,
how better by far,
bright and morning star
and you know me!
Who would ever believe
that someone like me
could ever know someone like you,
who spoke and the darkness had to flee
and you've shown us, and you've told us.

757 Capt. Alan J. Price, CA

We have come, we are here
to enter the presence of a holy God.
We have come, we are here
to enter the presence of a holy God.
In the name of Jesus, hear us as we pray;
come, Holy Spirit, teach us what to say.

We have come, we are here
to pray in the presence of a holy God.
We have come, we are here
to pray in the presence of a holy God,
to pray in the presence of a holy God.

This is a holy place, where Jesus meets
 us now.
This is a holy place, where the Spirit
 moves us now.

758 Colin Buchanan

Well, if you love the Lord
you can sing and shout.
And if you love the Lord
you can dance about.
But if you love the Lord
well you'd better obey,
'cause you got to do what the Lord say.

You got to do, wack-a-do, wack-a-do,
you got to do what the Lord say.
(Repeat)

Well if you love the Lord
sometimes you glad.
If you love the Lord
sometimes you sad.
If you love the Lord
well you'd better obey,
'cause you got to do what the Lord say.

Well Jesus laugh, and Jesus cry.
Jesus hurt and Jesus die.
But he rose from the dead
'cause he obey,
you know, he always do what the Lord
 say.

759 Dave Cooke

Well, I need to move this mountain,
but I've only got a toothpick.
And I need to move this ocean,
but I've only got a jug.
And I'm gonna build a building,
but all I've got is one brick.
You've gotta have faith, *that's right*
you've gotta have faith.

Continued overleaf

Well I need to take my dog for a walk,
but I haven't got a dog.
And I want to go fishing for a very big fish,
but all I've got is a piece of string.
And I want to sing so sweetly,
but I sound just like a frog.
You've gotta have faith, *that's right, yes sir, OK,*
you've gotta have faith.

Faith as small as an insect's nose,
as small as a mustard seed;
faith as tiny as a centipede's toes
that's how much you need.

Well I want to learn to love my friends,
but sometimes find that hard.
And I want to do the right thing,
but sometimes things get in the way.
And I want to do what God wants,
be always on my guard.
You've gotta have faith,
that's right, yes sir, OK, I said that's right,
you gotta have faith.

Well, I need to move this mountain,
but I've only got a toothpick.
And I need to move this ocean,
but I've only got a jug.
And I'm gonna build a building,
but all I've got is one brick.
You've gotta have faith,
that's right, yes sir, OK, I said that's right,
what's right? that's right!
You've gotta have faith. *(x4)*

© 2000 Daybreak Music Ltd.

760   Graham Kendrick

We'll walk the land with hearts on fire;
and ev'ry step will be a prayer.
Hope is rising, new day dawning;
sound of singing fills the air.

Two thousand years, and still the flame
is burning bright across the land.
Hearts are waiting, longing, aching,
for awak'ning once again.

Let the flame burn brighter,
in the heart of the darkness,
turning night to glorious day.
Let the song grow louder,
as our love grows stronger;
let it shine! Let it shine!

We'll walk for truth, speak out for love;
in Jesus' name we shall be strong,
to lift the fallen, to save the children,
to fill the nation with your song.

© 1989 Make Way Music

761   Gerry Holmes

Well you don't have to hear to listen,
you don't have to see to understand.
'Cause deep inside God has supplied
a little way of knowing.

And you don't have to touch to have feelings,
you don't have to smell to know lunch is near,
'cause deep inside God has supplied
a little seed that's growing.
Big people find it harder all the time
to listen to the inside.
'Cause most people say it's the cleverest way
to trust what's on the outside!

But you don't have to hear to listen,
you don't have to see to understand.
'Cause deep inside God has supplied
a little way of knowing,
hey yeah, yeah!

© 1986 Gerry Holmes. Willow Connection Pty. Ltd.

762 Steve Burnhope

We need to know the Bible,
if we want to know the Lord,
it isn't just a big old book,
the Bible is God's word,
it doesn't just have stories ('though the
  ones it has are true)
God put in all kinds of things
to speak to me and you.

  It reaches down into the soul,
  it reaches up into the mind,
  it reaches deep into the parts
  that other books cannot find,
  our spirits leap within us
  when we hear the word of God,
  that's why we need to know the Bible
  if we want to know the Lord.

There are sev'ral other ways
God can speak to us,
it may be when we're praying,
or through somebody else,
we should keep on praying
and list'ning to our friends,
but we need to know the Bible
to know what God intends.

God has many purposes
to accomplish through his word,
it helps us understand him,
and how much he loves the world,
it tells us when we're going wrong
and helps us find the way,
so when others ask, 'What is that book?'
this is what to say:

763 Monica O'Brien

We're God's family, God's children,
lift up your voice.
We're God's family, God's chosen,
let your heart rejoice!
United in the Spirit, united in the Son,
we'll be one for others! One in the Lord!

Have you ever been lonely,
bewildered by the way in which life's
  going?
Know it is true, someone is loving you.
Together we'll see it through.
Remember the hope that's been given to
  you.
So reach out! Reach out!
This way is true.

We are longing for wholeness.
Expand our minds to know the heart of
  Jesus.
Show us the way, reveal it this day.
Together as one we'll stay, claiming the
  joy
we've found in your name.
So reach out! Reach out!
We proclaim.

764 Dave Godfrey

We're going deep, deep, deep under the
  ocean,
we're going deep, deep, deep under the
  sea,
we're going deep, deep, deep in search
  of lasting treasure,
kept under the waves for me.

Continued overleaf

We're going deep, deep, deep no fear of
    danger,
we're going deep, deep, deep just hear
    the sound,
of the deep, deep, deep where the Lord
    of the sea
promises that he can be found.

It's not pirate loot, or ancient wrecks,
it's priceless what we seek.
It's lasting treasure, a friend for ever,
strength when we feel weak.

So we'll go deep, deep, deep under the
    ocean,
and we'll go deep, deep, deep until we
    know,
all the deep, deep love that he has for us:
deep is just where we have to go.

765 Andrew and Pauline Pearson

We're gonna build our lives on a solid
    rock,
build our lives on a solid rock,
we're gonna build our lives on a solid
    rock,
on Jesus Christ the Lord.
(Repeat)

We'll obey all he has to say
and do what he wants us to do,
then our lives will be secure:
Jesus living in me and you.

We're gonna build our lives on a solid
    rock,
build our lives on a solid rock,
we're gonna build our lives on a solid
    rock,
on Jesus Christ the Lord,
on Jesus Christ the Lord,
on Jesus Christ the Lord.
We said it's on Jesus, only on Jesus,
we're gonna build our lives alone.
We said it's on Jesus, only on Jesus,
we're gonna build our lives alone.

766 Garrie-John Barnes

We're gonna tell the world about Jesus!
We're gonna tell the world about who?
    Jesus!
We're gonna tell the world about Jesus!
And just how much he loves them.
We're gonna tell the world about Jesus!
We're gonna tell the world about who?
    Jesus!
We're gonna tell the world about,
dance and sing and shout about,
we're gonna tell the world about Jesus!

God is building up his kingdom;
does he want to use you and me? Yes!
God is building up his kingdom
to make it big and strong.
God is building up his kingdom;
does he want to use you and me? Yes!
God is gonna build it up,
never gonna give it up,
God is building up his kingdom.

767 Capt. Alan J. Price, CA

We're meeting with Jesus,
meeting the King, as we worship today;
we're meeting with Jesus,
meeting the King, as we sing and as
we pray.

Jesus knows our deepest thoughts,
the hopes and fears deep inside;
he longs to be our closest friend,
this King with arms open wide!
(Repeat)

768 J. D. Bullen

We're not too young to read about
 the stories in his word.
From a tiny babe in Bethlehem
to the risen Lord,
feeding of five thousand,
turning water into wine;
this is God's Son Jesus,
he's a friend of mine.

We're not too young, not too young,
we're not too young, not too young,
not too young. We're not too young,
N. T. Y. for J. E. S. U. S, Jesus.

Not yet old enough to vote,
or to take GCSEs,
we can't stay up all night
to watch TV.
Can't drive cars, get married,
or fly an aeroplane,
we can know for sure
that Jesus loves us just the same.

769 Phil Overton

We're raising the roof for Jesus,
raising the roof for Jesus.
We are the proof we're telling the truth,
we're raising the roof for Jesus.

We're building a wall for Jesus,
we're building a wall for Jesus,
we're standing up tall, we're not gonna fall,
we're building a wall for Jesus.

We'll open a door for Jesus,
we'll open a door for Jesus,
the eagle will soar, the lion will roar,
we'll open a door for Jesus.

We're raising the roof for Jesus,
building a wall for Jesus.
So, get off the floor and don't be a bore!
Give it some more – it isn't a chore.
The eagle will soar, the lion will roar!
We'll open a door . . . for Jesus.

770 Chris Jackson

We're the kids of the King,
that's why we dance and sing,
we're the kids, we're the kids, we're the
    kids of the King.
Oh yeah! Oh yeah!
(Repeat)

Come on ev'rybody, and join the
    celebration,
Jesus is our Lord and Saviour,
he's our King.
Clap your hands, dance your feet
and shout aloud to the Lord,
(Praise the Lord!) to the Lord (Praise the
    Lord!).
(We're the kids of the King! Yeah!)

771 Terry Tarsiuk

We sing a new song, we bless your name.
We sing a new song, we fan the flame.
The flame is burning, the flame is strong.
Your love's a fire, your love's my song.
Hallelujah, hallelujah,
hallelujah, hallelujah!

I sing a new song, unending praise.
I sing a new song, of eternal grace.
Your voice like honey, smooth as silk.
Says you love me, I'm in your will.
Glory to God, glory to God,
glory to God, glory to God.

© 2001 Celestial Arts Inc.

772 Paul Crouch and David Mudie

We stand together with our feet upon
a rock,
we stand together with our feet upon
a rock,
we stand together with our feet upon
a rock,
it's a rock which never can be moved,
it's a rock which never can be moved.

Mountains may crumble, storms may
lash and rage,
but this rock never shall be moved.
The sun may darken, the moon not give
its light,
but this rock never shall be,
never shall be moved!

Our friends may fail us and
disappointments come,
but this rock never shall be moved!
You may start wondering what it's all
about,
but this rock never shall be moved!

We stand together with our feet upon
a rock,
we stand together with our feet upon
a rock,
we stand together with our feet upon
a rock,
it's a rock which never can be moved,
it's a rock which never can be moved.

© 2001 Daybreak Music Ltd.

773 Unknown

What a mighty God we serve,
what a mighty God we serve;
angels bow before him,
heaven and earth adore him,
what a mighty God we serve.

774 James Wright

What wondrous love is this
from heav'n to earth come down?
The greatest gift of all was given,
the holy Lamb of God
was lifted up to die
that we might have life.

What wondrous pow'r is this
that held you to that cross?
Not the agony of thorns and nails,
but everlasting love
and waves of holy grace
poured out for us all.

Upon a cross of shame
you bled and died,
poured out your life
with arms open wide,
and there you hung
with a heart full of love
poured out for all the world,
with a heart full of love.

Your blood for ever flows,
a never-failing stream
of forgiveness, of pow'r and cleansing.
And your cross for ever stands
from age to age the same,
drawing all men to you.

Upon a cross of shame
you bled and died,
poured out your life
with arms open wide,
and there you hung
with a heart full of love
poured out for all the world,
with a heart full of love.
Poured out for all the world,
with a heart full of love;
poured out for all the world,
with a heart full of love.

775 Nick Harding

When I smile or rub my hair,
when my arms wave ev'rywhere,
when I jump high in the air,
I know God is there,
oh yes, I do!
I know God is there.

When I've had a nasty scare,
when there's no one anywhere,
when my best friend will not share,
I know God is there,
oh yes, I do!
I know God is there.

776 Steve and Kay Morgan-Gurr

When Jesus taught his friends to pray,
he taught them how to live:
forgiving others the same way
they'd like him to forgive.

And if we know that we're forgiven,
we'll want to show it by our love,
and try to grow to be like we should be,
living to please our God above.

When we forgive, it helps us see
what Father God has done:
forgiving you, forgiving me,
through Jesus, his dear Son.

777 Colin Buchanan

When the fists are flying and the baby's
  crying,
and your blood's at a hundred degrees.
When the screen-door's open and you're
  just not coping,
and you can't see the wood for the
  trees.
When you're right on the verge of
  flipping your lid
don't take it out on the other kids.

It's time for a whole lotta self-control.
It's time to fix your eyes on the
  heavenly goal.
It's time to keep in step with the Spirit,
if you've gone and put your big foot
  in it.
Confess your sin and consider the
  good of your soul.
And pray for a whole lotta self-
  control.

When you bite your tongue and you
  hammer your thumb,
and your brain is starting to ache.
When the traffic's crawling and the
  mower's stalling,
and you're just about fit to break.
When you're getting hassled beyond
  belief
don't give ev'rybody else the grief.

Continued overleaf

It's time for a whole lotta self-control.
It's time to fix your eyes on the
   heavenly goal.
It's time to keep in step with the Spirit,
if you've gone and put your big foot
   in it.
Confess your sin and consider the
   good of your soul.
And pray for a whole lotta self-
   control.

When the insults hurt and you're down
   in the dirt,
and you're just about to rant and rave,
remember Christ who paid the price
and took your place in the grave.
You can go ballistic, pull out your hair,
or commit yourself into his care.

778   Jenny-Jenny/Chris Jackson

When the Holy Spirit comes upon you,
you will be filled with power.
When the Holy Spirit comes upon you,
you will be filled with power.
Power to live, power to love,
power to do all that God commands you,
power to speak, power to heal,
power to fight the enemy.

779   Matt Redman

When the music fades,
all is stripped away,
and I simply come.
Longing just to bring
something that's of worth
that will bless your heart.

I'll bring you more than a song,
for a song in itself
is not what you have required.
You search much deeper within,
through the way things appear;
you're looking into my heart.

   I'm coming back to the heart of
      worship,
   and it's all about you,
   all about you, Jesus.
   I'm sorry, Lord,
   for the thing I've made it,
   when it's all about you,
   all about you, Jesus.

King of endless worth,
no one could express
how much you deserve.
Though I'm weak and poor
all I have is yours,
every single breath.

I'll bring you . . .

780   Gerry Holmes

When the sky turned black and Jesus
   cried,
that was a kind of victory.
When the temple curtain was ripped
   apart,
that was a sign for you and me.

   It was a Good Fri, Good Fri,
      Good Friday,
   it was a Good Fri, Good Friday.
   (Repeat)

When his friends all turned and ran away,
the soldiers nailed his hands and feet.
On a lonely hill on a lonely day,
Jesus died for you and me.

On a Good Fri . . .

When there's hat parades and Easter eggs
and hot cross buns are in the stores
we remember Jesus on the cross,
we remember who he suffered for.

Remember Good Fri . . .

781 Chris Jackson and Jill Hoffman

Where the presence of the Lord is,
there is freedom, freedom, freedom.
Where the presence of the Lord is,
there is freedom in the presence of the
    Lord.
There is healing and forgiveness,
there is freedom and release.
There is joy and peace and laughter
that will never cease.
So let's give him all our worries;
let us give him all our fears,
for we know that he is with us
and we know he always hears.

782 Nahum Tate, alt.

While shepherds watched their flocks by
    night,
all seated on the ground,
the angel of the Lord came down,
and glory shone around.

'Fear not,' said he, (for mighty dread
had seized their troubled mind);
'glad tidings of great joy I bring
to you and all mankind.

'To you in David's town this day
is born of David's line
a Saviour, who is Christ the Lord;
and this shall be the sign:

'The heav'nly babe you there shall find
to human view displayed,
all meanly wrapped in swathing bands,
and in a manger laid.'

Thus spake the seraph, and forthwith
appeared a shining throng
of angels praising God, who thus
addressed their joyful song:

'All glory be to God on high,
and to the earth be peace,
goodwill henceforth from heav'n to earth
begin and never cease.'

783 Stuart Townend

Who paints the skies into glorious day?
Only the splendour of Jesus.
Who breathes his life into fists of clay?
Only the splendour of Jesus.
Who shapes the valleys and brings the
    rain?
Only the splendour of Jesus.
Who makes the desert to live again?
Only the splendour of Jesus.

Teach ev'ry nation his marv'llous ways;
each generation shall sing his praise.

He is wonderful, he is glorious,
clothed in righteousness,
full of tenderness.
Come and worship him,
he's the Prince of life,
he will cleanse our hearts in his river
*   of fire.*

Continued overleaf

Who hears the cry of the barren one?
Only the mercy of Jesus.
Who breaks the curse of the heart of
   stone?
Only the mercy of Jesus.
Who storms the prison and sets men
   free?
Only the mercy of Jesus.
Purchasing souls for eternity?
Only the mercy of Jesus.

He is wonderful, he is glorious,
clothed in righteousness,
full of tenderness.
Come and worship him,
he's the Prince of life,
he will cleanse our hearts in his river
   of fire.

784 Susie Hare

Why do fish swim instead of sink?
Why does a camel store its drink?
Why do hens cluck instead of coo?
Why do cars purr instead of moo?

Well, I don't know why they do it,
so it's no good asking me.
It's the way that God has made them,
and it just comes naturally!

Why do bees buzz instead of bark?
Why does an owl see in the dark?
Why do birds fly instead of walk?
Why do pigs grunt instead of talk?

Why do sheep chew instead of peck?
Why do giraffes have great long necks?
Why do mice squeak instead of roar?
Why does a woodworm eat the door?

785 Nick Harding

Will you follow the Shepherd who knows
   the way?
Will you follow the King from above?
Will you follow the Shepherd ev'ry day?
Will you follow the God of love?

I will follow the God of love,
I will follow him.
(Repeat)

Will you look for the light that shows the
   way?
Will you look for the King from above?
Will you look for the Light of the World
   today?
Will you look for the God of love?

I will look for the God of love,
I will look for him.
(Repeat)

786 Andy Read

With all of my heart I love you, Lord;
with all of my soul I love you, Lord;
with all of my mind I love you, Lord;
with all of the strength that is within.
(Repeat)

There is no greater thing I could do in
   all my life,
there is no greater cost to make.
There is no greater joy that you want to
   give to me
when I have you reigning in my life.

787 James Wright

With all of my heart I will praise.
With all of my heart I will praise.
With all of my heart I will lift up his holy
name.
With all of my heart I will praise.
(Repeat)

With all of my being I will rejoice in the
Lord.
With all of my being I will give praise to
the name of Jesus.

With all of my breath I will sing . . .

With both of my hands I will clap . . .

With both of my feet I will jump . . .

With all of my body I'll dance . . .

Praise the Lord, hallelujah.
Praise the Lord, hallelujah.
Praise the Lord, hallelujah.
Praise the Lord, hallelujah.
Praise the Lord.
(Repeat)

788 Martin Cooper

With just one touch,
you have made the earth and the sea.
With just one breath
you created the sun and the sky,
and you have made all the good things
in my life,
you are there whenever I cry.

For you are Lord of all,
and your love goes on for ever;
you are Lord of all,
and my life I will surrender to you.

And in my life
I will sing my praise to you,
and with my lips
I will only say things that are true,
and I will speak of the good things you
have made,
you are with me every day.

789 Olivia Johnson

Wobble your knees, wiggle your nose,
look with your eyes and listen with your
ears,
'cos God is all around us, and he loves
you and me
and you and you and you.

So wobble your knees, wiggle your nose,
look with your eyes and listen with your
ears,
'cos God is all around us, and he loves
you and me
and you and you and you and me.

790 Chris Jackson

Worship the King, your praises bring
right into the presence of the Lord.
No need to fear, you can draw near,
and stand in the presence of the Lord.

Saying 'I love you, Lord',
saying 'I love you, Lord',
saying 'I love you, Lord'.
(Repeat)

'I love you Lord'.

791 Phil Chapman

Wow! That's amazing.
Wow! That's fantastic.
When Jesus died, he died to forgive me.
Wow! That's amazing.
Wow! That's fantastic.
God's love for us is big as big can be.

The Bible says we all do wrong things,
we displease God, we disobey him,
but God loves us so much, he's given us
  a way
to put right the wrong things that we do
  and say.

God sent his Son, his name is Jesus,
he died upon a cross to save us.
There is no other way to gain eternal life
and to be with God in heaven when we
  die.

I must trust Jesus as my Saviour,
live my life for him, change my behaviour.
He says he will forgive me, of that I can
  be sure,
and I'll live with him in heav'n for
  evermore!

792 Chris Jackson

You are my God and my Father;
you are my Lord and my King.
You are my friend and my Saviour;
I will lift my voice and sing;
fill me up and let your Spirit flow,
fill me up, let the love of Jesus show,
'cause I want to be like Jesus, he's my
  King.

793 Paul Crouch and David Mudie

You are the potter, I am the clay,
your hands are working in my life day by
  day,
and as they are moving I am made anew,
built up and moulded 'til I'm closer to
  the image of you.

794 James Wright

You came from heaven's splendour
to earth's humanity,
healing the broken-hearted,
setting them free.
But for the joy that followed,
you gave up ev'rything;
death on a cursèd cross
that we might have life.

Jesus, almighty Saviour,
you rose up from the dead,
victorious, triumphant,
just like you said.
In resurrection power,
the grave you overcame,
and now you sit in heaven,
for evermore to reign.

There in the tomb your broken
body in silence lay,
but for three days, three nights
it did not see decay.
You had a greater purpose,
you had a greater plan,
that through the death of one man
all might have life.

795 Colin Buchanan

You can tell the Lord that you love
him any time.
You can tell the Lord that you need
him any time.
Thank him for his love and care,
shoot him up an arrow prayer.
You can tell the Lord that you love
him any time.

In the middle of whatever you're doing
at school,
at lunch when you're kickin' the ball.
When you're chasing your mates all over
the place
you can talk to the Lord of all.

When you're happy as Larry, when you're
full of joy.
When you're blown out by the view.
Give thanks to the God who's showered
his blessings ,
showered his blessings on you, and you,
and you, and . . .

You can tell the Lord that you love him.
You can tell the Lord that you need him.
You can tell the Lord that you love him
any time.

796 J. Gowans

You can't stop rain from falling down,
prevent the sun from shining;
you can't stop spring from coming in,
or winter from resigning.
Or still the waves or stay the winds,
or keep the day from dawning;
you can't stop God from loving you,
his love is new each morning.

You can't stop ice from being cold,
you can't stop fire from burning;
or hold the tide that's going out,
delay its sure returning.
Or halt the progress of the years,
the flight of fame and fashion;
you can't stop God from loving you,
his nature is compassion.

You can't stop God from loving you,
though you may disobey him;
you can't stop God from loving you,
however you betray him.
From love like this no pow'r on earth
the human heart can sever;
you can't stop God from loving you,
not God, not now, nor ever.

797 Terry Tarsiuk

You gave a guarantee, I've been
chosen,
I have a destiny; you paid the price for
me,
I'm your chosen, I have a destiny.

Chosen in you before the world began;
created for you by your loving hand.
I have been blessed so I give you my best
and I live with the joy of knowing I give
you pleasure.

798 Doug Horley

You need to natter to God,
because you matter to God,
because he loves to hear
just what you are thinking.
(Repeat)

Continued overleaf

*His heart leaps ev'ry time he hears
    you talking,
his heart leaps ev'ry time he hears
    you sing.
He's so thrilled when you tell him that
    you love him,
keep talk, talk, talking, talk, talk,
    talking to the King.*

799 Nick Harding

You offer a way
to live day by day
in peace and in purity,
but Jesus, I know
that I need to grow
to love you completely.

*From all fears, pain and tears,
Jesus, set me free.
When I'm shouting, fearing, doubting,
still the storm in me.*

I know deep inside
the times I have tried
to change, but I stay the same,
so now I give way
and offer today
my life, as you call my name.

800 Gerry Holmes

You're a mighty God, yes, and mighty
    strong,
who can change the world,
even beat King Kong,
and you care for us in so many ways.
If we trust and pray, we will grow and
    change.

801 Paul Field
based on Psalm 104

*You ride on the wings of the wind,
you are wonderful, Lord. The glory is
    yours.
All of creation begins by your wisdom
    and might;
clothed in majesty and light
 you ride on the wings of the wind.*

When I hear the voice of your thunder,
when I see your lightning in the sky,
by the light of ev'ry star
I see how wonderful you are.
All my life I will sing your praise.

By the moon you measure the seasons,
by the sun you measure out the days:
all of nature plays a part,
bringing heaven to my heart.
All my life I will sing your praise.

802 Dave Godfrey

*Your love, O Lord, is higher than the
    mountains.
Your love, O Lord, is deeper than the
    sea.
Your love, O Lord, is wider than the
    universe,
your love, O Lord, it sustains me.*

You are love, kind and patient,
mighty arms protect me today.
As I am, I'm loved by you,
so when I feel my feet a-slipping,
I'll just say that your love . . .

Nothing, Lord, in all creation
could ever take your love away.
I'm so glad I'm loved by you,
so when I feel my feet a-dancing,
I'll just say that your love . . .

803 Brian Doerksen and Brenton Brown

Your love is amazing, steady and
  unchanging,
your love is a mountain, firm beneath my
  feet.
Your love is a myst'ry, how you gently lift
  me,
when I am surrounded, your love carries
  me.

Hallelujah, hallelujah,
hallelujah, your love makes me sing.
Hallelujah, hallelujah,
hallelujah, your love makes me sing.

Your love is surprising, I can feel it rising,
all the joy that's growing deep inside of
  me.
Ev'ry time I see you, all your goodness
  shines through,
I can feel this God-song, rising up in me.

Hallelujah, hallelujah,
hallelujah, your love makes me sing.
Hallelujah, hallelujah,
hallelujah, your love makes me sing.
Yes, you make me sing.
Lord you make me sing, sing, sing.
How you make me sing.

Hallelujah, hallelujah,
hallelujah, your love makes me sing.
Hallelujah, hallelujah,
hallelujah, your love makes me sing.

804 Brian Edgeley

You've gotta be fit (fit!) for the King,
giving your life to him
Fit, (fit!) for the King in ev'ry way;
heart, mind and soul;
living your life for him.
Fit, (fit!) for the King every day! (x3)

Reach up high and touch the sky,
bend down low and touch your toes,
open up your arms and heart to Jesus!
Lift your arms to worship him,
clap your hands to praise him;
open up your heart and mind to him.

805 John Matheson

You've touched my life,
I can never be the same.
You've touched my life,
you're in my heart to reign.
You've touched my life,
all glory to your name.
You've touched my life,
you've touched my life.

806 Doug Horley

You won't get to heaven on the back of
  a camel
and you won't get to heaven on a sheep.
You won't get to heaven on a double
  decker bus,
and you won't get to heaven in a jeep.
A pogo stick will only make you feel sick
and you can't drive there in a car.
A rocket in your pocket might make you
  see stars
but it sure won't get you that far.

There's only one way (one way), one
  way (one way),
you can get to heaven, oh yeah!
There's only one way (one way), one
  way (one way),
that's through God's Son Jesus.
He's the only way.

Continued overleaf

You won't get to heaven by looking real
good
and you won't get to heaven 'cos you're
slick.
You won't get to heaven by jumping
from a plane
and by flapping your arms real quick.
A flight or a kite or an elastic band
might whizz you through the air.
Or you could scuttle in a shuttle right
over the moon,
but it still won't get you there.

*There's only one way (one way), one
way (one way),
you can get to heaven, oh yeah!
There's only one way (one way), one
way (one way),
that's through God's Son Jesus.
He's the only way.*

You won't get to heaven by saying
you're a Christian
and you won't get to heaven 'cos you're
good.
You won't get to heaven just by going to
a church
though many may think you could.
A mum or a dad or a sister who loves
Jesus
won't get you there, it's true.
Oh, you're in favour with the Saviour but
this you gotta know,
you need to find him just for you.

Key Word Index

The key word categories appear alphabetically and are cross-referenced to make it as easy as possible for worship leaders to find songs and hymns suitable for various themes and occasions.

POWER

See **Holy Spirit - Power**

PRAISE

UNITY

See **Church**

WITNESSING

See **Evangelism**

WORSHIP

Index of First Lines and Titles

This index gives the first line of each hymn. If a hymn is known by an alternative title, this is also given, but indented and in italics.

Acknowledgements

The publishers wish to express their gratitude to the following for permission to include copyright material in this publication. Details of copyright owners are given underneath each individual song.

Robyn Barnett, 4 Heathcote Road, Twickenham, Middlesex, TW1 1RX.

Bucks Music Ltd., Onward House, 11 Uxbridge Road, London W8 7TQ.

Celestial Arts Inc., PO Box 98800, Seattle, WA 98198, USA.

Mrs J. Chedgey, 40 Neville Close, Basingstoke, Hampshire, RG21 3HQ.

Christian Education Publications, St Andrews House, Sydney Square, PO Box A287, Sydney South, NSW 1235, Australia.

Christian Faith Centre, PO Box 98800, Seattle, WA 98198, USA.

CopyCare Ltd., PO Box 77, Hailsham, East Sussex, BN27 3EF, UK on behalf of Mission Hills Music, Alliance Media Ltd., Word Music, Maranatha! Music, Mercy/Vineyard Publishing/Music Services, Chris Falson Music, CN Publishing, Whole World Publishing, Rettino Kerner Publishing, CA Music/Music Services, Fan into Flame Ministries, Hope Publishing Co, Meadowgreen Music/ EMI Christian Music Publishing, Salvationist Publishing & Supplies, Vineyard Songs (UK/Eire), Word's Spirit of Praise Music, and Soundtree Music.

Daybreak Music, Silverdale Road, Eastbourne, East Sussex, BN20 7AB.

Dyba Music, Süthers Garten 14, 45130 Essen, Germany.

John Hardwick, 12 Normanton Way, Histon, Cambridgeshire, CB4 9XS.

Paul Herbert, 79 Bramford Road, Ipswich, Suffolk, IP1 2LT.

Ice Music Ltd., Bayley's Plantation, St Philip, Barbados, W. Indies.

Iona Community, Community House, Pearce Institute, Govan, Glasgow, G51 3UU.

IQ Music Ltd., Commercial House, 52 Perrymount Road, Haywards Heath, West Sussex, RH16 3DT.

Jubilate Hymns, 4 Thorne Park Road, Chelston, Torquay, TQ2 6RX.

Kingsway's Thankyou Music, PO Box 75, Eastbourne, East Sussex, BN23 6NW, UK, on behalf of Kingsway's Thankyou Music, Celebration (Europe & British Commonwealth, excl. Canada, Australasia & Africa), Little Misty Music (Worldwide, excl. Australia & New Zealand), Arise Ministries (Europe & British Commonwealth, excl. Australasia & Canada), Glorie Music (Worldwide, excl. N. America), Sound Truth Publishing (Europe & British Commonwealth, excl. Canada), Darlene Zschech/Hillsongs, the songs of Ian Smale (Worldwide, excl. USA & Canada).

Kings Church Creative Ministries, 69 Lower Dock Street, Newport, South Wales, NP20 1EH.

Leosong Copyright Services, 13 Berners Street, London, W1T 3LH.

Mr J. MacPherson, 20 Megalong Road, Nedlands, W. Australia.

Make Way Music, PO Box 263, Croydon, Surrey, CR9 5AP. International copyright secured. All rights reserved.

Mr P. Mangold, PO Box 12, Belgrave, Victoria 3160, Australia.

Mr Robin Mann, 54 Currawong Crescent, Modbury Heights, SA 5092, Australia.

Music Sales, 8/9 Frith Street, London, W1V 5TZ. All rights reserved. International copyright secured.

OCP Publications, 5536 NE Hassalo, Portland, OR 97213, USA. All rights reserved. Used by permission.

Out of the Ark Music, Sefton House, 2 Molesey Road, Walton-on-Thames, Surrey, KT12 4RQ.

Oxford University Press, Great Clarendon Street, Oxford, OX2 6DP, from Enlarged Songs of Praise, 1931.

Powerpack/Learning Curve Music, PO Box 421, Hailsham, East Sussex, BN27 4ZA.

Restoration Music, PO Box 356, Leighton Buzzard, LU7 3WP.

RiverSong Music, PO Box 301, Windsor, NSW 2756, Australia.

Scripture Union, 207-209 Queensway, Bletchley, Milton Keynes, Bucks., MK2 2EB.

Sea Dream Music, PO Box 13533, London, E7 0SG, UK.

Sovereign Music UK, PO Box 356, Leighton Buzzard, LU7 3WP.

Sovereign Lifestyle Music, PO Box 356, Leighton Buzzard, LU7 3WP.

Stainer & Bell Ltd., PO Box 110, Victoria House, 23 Gruneisen Road, Finchley, London, N3 1DZ.

Universal Music Publishing Pty. Ltd., 3 Munn Reserve, Millers Point, NSW 2000, Australia.

Josef Weinberger Ltd., 12-14 Mortimer Street, London, W1T 3JJ.

Wellingborough Christian Centre, 13 Alliance Terrace, Wellingborough, Northants., NN8 4RA.

Windswept Pacific Music, Hope House, 40 St Peter's Road, London, W6.